## YEAR 1  TERM 2

# Lesson Plans

with
## Homework and other Copymasters

OXFORD
UNIVERSITY PRESS

*Oxford Maths Zone* is the outcome of a large team effort from many contributors, with a wide range of backgrounds from practising classroom teachers to teacher trainers and Consultants in the National Numeracy Strategy. The project director is Stephen Ashton, and the team of contributors for the infant years materials is:

| | |
|---|---|
| Bill Bairstow | Teresa MacDonald |
| Roger Bird | Margaret McDougall |
| Rae Cook | Roz McEwan |
| Marian Di Nardo | Liz McMullen |
| Robin Foster | Alison Meechan |
| Frieda Fraser | Jeanette Mumford |
| Lesley Ireland | Carol Roberts |
| Cath Kendall | Mary Ruddle |
| Lindsay Logan | Angela Speirs |
| Margaret Williams | Mary Wilkinson |

# OXFORD
**UNIVERSITY PRESS**

Great Clarendon Street, Oxford OX2 6DP

Oxford University Press is a department of the University of Oxford.
It furthers the University's objective of excellence in research, scholarship, and education by publishing worldwide in

Oxford  New York

Athens  Auckland  Bangkok  Bogotá  Buenos Aires  Calcutta
Cape Town  Chennai  Dar es Salaam  Delhi  Florence  Hong Kong  Istanbul
Karachi  Kuala Lumpur  Madrid  Melbourne  Mexico City  Mumbai
Nairobi  Paris  São Paulo  Singapore  Taipei  Tokyo  Toronto  Warsaw
with associated companies in Berlin  Ibadan

Oxford is a registered trade mark of Oxford University Press
in the UK and in certain other countries

British Library Cataloguing in Publication Data

Data available

ISBN 0 19 836035 5

Designed and typeset by Oxford Designers and Illustrators
Printed in Great Britain

# Welcome to *Oxford Maths Zone!*

The aim of *Oxford Maths Zone* is to make effective maths teaching easier. As you look through these resources and become familiar with them, you will see how they can contribute to the development of an enriched and successful maths environment – a *Maths Zone* – in your classroom.

Based on the curriculum objectives and teaching strategies outlined by the *National Numeracy Strategy* (and *Improving Maths 5–14* in Scotland), we set out to bring clarity, simplicity and warmth to their delivery in the classroom. The resources for children from ages 4 to 7 consist of four inter-related components: *Lesson Plans with Homework and other Copymasters, Big Books, Shared Activity Books* and *Recording Books*. Each term features a linked set of these components.

## Lesson Plans with Homework and other Copymasters

This book provides the essential framework round which the other resources are based. It has these main features:

**Units:** the two-page spreads that start on page 10 present **Units** of work (usually a week long) which map exactly into the National objectives.
**Lesson Plans:** each unit offers a sequence of daily **Lesson Plans** with an emphasis throughout on clear learning objectives.
**Mental Activities:** for each Lesson Plan, there are lively mental activities, briefly expressed and linked into a logical unfolding sequence and derived from a bank of general strategies (given on pages 34–35).
**Main Session:** usually three activities are suggested, ranging as appropriate between whole class, group and individual approaches. All feature suggestions for open-ended stimulus questions and present clear links into the other resources provided by *Oxford Maths Zone*.
**Plenary:** each Lesson Plan ends with suggestions for ways to handle the **Plenary** session, helping the children to focus on key ideas.
**Copymasters:** at the back of this Lesson Plans book, the **Copymasters** provide helpful support for each unit in a variety of formats; and the **Homework Copymasters** offer a simple way for children to practise key ideas as they share them at home.

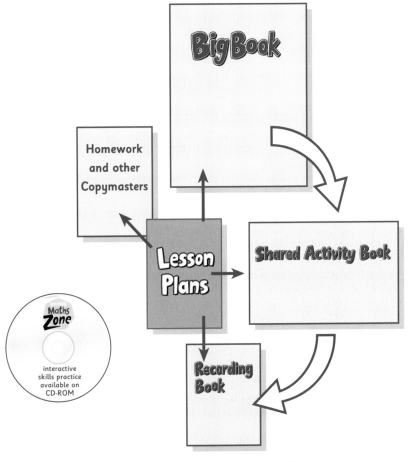

The *Lesson Plans* help you to make best use of the other resources

Each term is divided into units

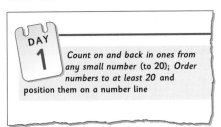

The units are divided into lessons. The key objectives are in *italic*.

## Daily lesson structure

| Mental | Main Session | Plenary |
|---|---|---|
| Clap and Count: to 30<br>Before and After: one before / after any given number to 20 | • **Counting on and back in ones: Big B**<br>The children are at the swimming pool: d<br>happening at the desk. Ask children to rea | *Did you land on a swimmer, Joe? Which<br>many did you count back from there? Wh<br>did Joe have to move back to?* |
| Details of how to play the mental activities are given on pages 34–35 | A sequence of suggested key activities is offered for each lesson | Ways to pull the class together and focus on key ideas are also given |

## Big Books

These stimulus picture books present realistic, light-hearted introductions to the main ideas in each unit, and facilitate discussion and exploration. They enable interactive discussion with the children, reveal a lot about their insights, and provide a focus for the unit's activity. They are also funny – children will delight in exploring the sometimes all-too-real situations that are presented!

## Shared Activity Book

After the *Lesson Plan* notes and *Big Book* pages have supported you in exploring new ideas, the *Shared Activity Book* provides engaging ways for children to practise new ideas. Each page of the *Shared Activity Book* provides a 'gameboard' on which two children work co-operatively. Moving counters or other simple apparatus round the board helps them to talk and work together to grasp the new idea, with no need for them to make written records. For each activity, extension and simplification ideas are suggested; many others are possible.

## Recording Book

This name (as opposed to 'workbook') reflects an important change in focus. At about half the bulk of conventional workbook provision, the *Recording Book* has been developed with two objectives in mind. First, to enable children to move on from concrete examples to the more abstract ideas that lie at the heart of mathematical understanding; and second, to provide evidence for themselves and others that they have indeed grasped the new ideas they have been exploring. The *Recording Book* does not set out to 'teach' new ideas – books can never do that. But it does set out to clarify ideas and to enable children to 'show off' the understanding they have acquired, without being burdened by a lot of writing. Some children may want to make informal written records of their mental calculations. This is to be encouraged where appropriate. The rear cover provides a record of work done which links directly into the class record sheet (CM25). Both link directly to National Numeracy Strategy objectives.

## Copymasters and Homework Copymasters

Mainly, the Copymaster sheets provide cards or other items to be cut out and used at various points. The Homework Copymasters enable children to share and practise new ideas at home. The homework activities reflect a main idea from the units and therefore are best used towards the end of each unit, typically on a Thursday. The icon **▐▌** is a reminder that a Homework Sheet is available.

## *Oxford Maths Zone* and the *National Numeracy Strategy*

In developing *Oxford Maths Zone* we have taken the approach, content, and sequence of the *National Numeracy Strategy* very seriously – and have added into this the necessary creativity and detail that will ensure a successful maths environment in your classroom. The *National Numeracy Strategy* and *Scottish Improving Maths 5–14* set out ambitious, worthwhile objectives for maths teaching. In summary, these are:

- clear yearly, termly, weekly and daily objectives
- a lesson structure that incorporates time for mental, main session and plenary time each day
- a lively pace, linked to frequent repetition of key ideas
- frequent, structured mental maths
- interactive teacher–children dialogue
- emphasis on children working co-operatively
- reduced emphasis on written outcomes.

All of these characteristics are reflected in the *Oxford Maths Zone* structure. The *Lesson Plans* reflect the focus on clarity of objective, lesson structure, pace, and mental activity; the *Big Books*, *Shared Activity Books* and *Recording Books* support effective classroom practice in the different aspects of children's learning.

The *Big Book* pictures stimulate focused discussion

The *Shared Activity Book* pages enable practice of new ideas

The *Recording Book* pages consolidate new ideas and 'show off' understanding

*Copymasters* are used in a variety of ways...

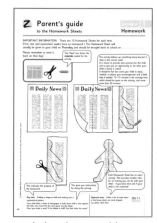
...including homework!

## Using *Oxford Maths Zone* in the classroom

**Clear sequence:** The clarity of the *Oxford Maths Zone* structure offers its own opportunities. If you are not a maths 'expert', *Oxford Maths Zone* offers the security that the *National Numeracy Strategy Framework for Teaching Mathematics* is being covered in a coherent, logical way. If you want to tackle the *Framework* in a different sequence, it is very easy to find the location where each of the objectives is tackled using the planning charts given on pages 6–7. None of the activities are 'compulsory': our hope is that there will be many occasions where you say, 'I can think of a different way to do that'... and we would encourage this attitude. But it is our belief that the clear structure offered by *Oxford Maths Zone* is the best way to make this personal approach succeed.

**Parallel structure:** In Years 1 and 2, the weekly planning sequence suggested by the *Framework for Teaching Mathematics* is very similar: the content in Year 2 Term 1 is a re-visiting and extension of Year 1 Term 1. Because *Oxford Maths Zone* exactly follows this recommended sequence, if you have a mixed-age class, the possibility for fruitful mental, main and plenary sessions where the children 'feed' off one another is greatly increased. If you wish to have children working on the same topic but at a more straightforward level, it is easy to see where appropriate resources can be found: usually, it is in the corresponding unit, but you can always check in the planning grid.

**Key ideas:** for every topic, we have supplied a range of strategies for approaching each key idea, with frequent suggestions for simplifying and extending them. But the focus is always on the key ideas: simplifications are provided to ensure that the key idea is grasped. Where there are natural opportunities for lateral extension of key ideas, these are noted in the *Lesson Plans*. These become more frequent as the children move through Year 2. We have not generally encouraged 'forward' extensions, preferring children to have a firm grasp of current key ideas, rather than be introduced early to new ideas to which they will have to return later anyway. Building on the objective of maintaining a brisk pace, none of the activities in *Oxford Maths Zone* needs to last more than 10–15 minutes: because of this, the management problem of keeping faster-working children purposefully occupied is minimal.

| | Year 1 Term 1: Topic and | |
| --- | --- | --- |
| | | page num |
| unit (days) | Framework for Teaching Mathematics • Topics | Lesson Plans |
| 1 (3) | • Counting, properties of numbers and number sequences • Place value and ordering | pgs 8–9 |
| 2 (5) | • Counting, properties of numbers and number sequences • Place value and ordering • Understanding addition; Rapid recall of addition facts; | pgs 10–11 |

The structure in Year 1 Term 1 is similar to...

| | Year 2 Term 1: Topic and | |
| --- | --- | --- |
| | | page num |
| unit (days) | Framework for Teaching Mathematics • Topics | Lesson Plans |
| 1 (3) | • Counting, properties of numbers and number sequences • Place value and ordering | pgs 8–9 |
| 2 (5) | • Counting, properties of numbers and number sequences • Place value and ordering • Understanding addition; Rapid recall of addition facts; | pgs 10–11 |

...the structure in Year 2 Term 1

## Making *Oxford Maths Zone* work for you

Every teacher will use the resources provided by *Oxford Maths Zone* differently. In developing this package of resources we have set out to make effective teaching easier, whatever your teaching style. Ask yourself the questions that we have asked ourselves:

- Have we kept the planning structure clear and simple?
- Are we facilitating better dialogue, built on clear objectives, open questioning and engaging *Big Book* stimulus resources?
- Do we succeed in offering an effective mental maths strategy, utilising daily mental sessions that the children will think of as games, and continual reinforcement as children enjoy the *Shared Activity Book*?
- By confining writing in the *Recording Book* to the times when it is most valuable, are we encouraging children's confidence?
- Do the *Homework Sheets* offer a simple but effective way for communicating with parents?
- Are the children remaining enthusiastic as they grow in mathematical skill?

Well... of course we hope so! Certainly, the belief that we have something important to offer has kept us all going through the very intensive developmental process. Your comments on our work will always be appreciated. Keep in touch via the *Oxford Maths Zone* care-line at Oxford University Press – the telephone number is on the back cover. Our hope is that by using these materials, you and the children in your care will be enabled to work together effectively. Enjoy your time together in the *Oxford Maths Zone*!

**Stephen Ashton**
*Oxford Maths Zone* **project director**

# National Numeracy Strategy:

## Framework Planner for Year 1

| | Term 1 | Term 2 | Term 3 | Mental |
|---|---|---|---|---|
| **Numbers and the number system** | | | | |
| *Counting, properties of numbers and number sequences* | | | | |
| Know the number names and recite them in order to at least 20, from and back to zero. | 1 | 1 | 1 | M |
| **Count reliably at least 20 objects.** | 1, 8 | 1, 7 | 8, 14 | |
| Describe and extend number sequences: **count on and back in ones from any small number,** | 2, 3, 8 | 1 | | M2 M3 |
| **and in tens from and back to zero;** | 8 | 1 | | M |
| count on in twos from zero, then one, | | 1, 8 | 1 | |
| and begin to recognise odd or even numbers to about 20 as 'every other number'; | | 1, 8 | 1 | |
| count in steps of 5 from zero to 20 or more, then back again; | | 8, 13 | 1, 7 | |
| begin to count on in steps of 3 from zero. | | | 1, 7, 8 | |
| *Place value and ordering* | | | | |
| **Read and write numerals from 0 to at least 20.** | 1, 2, 8, 14 | 2, 14 | 8,14 most | M |
| Begin to know what each digit in a two-digit number represents. | 9, 14 | 2, 9 | 9 | M |
| Partition a 'teens' number and | 9 | 9 | 9 | M |
| begin to partition larger two-digit numbers into a multiple of ten and ones (TU). | | 9, 13 | 9 | M2 M3 |
| **Understand and use the vocabulary of comparing and ordering numbers,** | 2 | 2 | 2, 9 | M |
| including ordinal numbers to at least 20. | 9 | | 2, 9 | |
| Use the = sign to represent equality. | 2, 3 | 9, most | most | |
| Compare two familiar numbers, say which is more or less, and give a number which lies between them. | | | 2 | M |
| **Within the range 0 to 30, say the number that is 1 or 10 more or less than any given number.** | 8 | 2, 7 | | M |
| **Order numbers to at least 20, and position them on a number line.** | 2 | 1, 2 | 2, 7, 9 | M |
| *Estimating* | | | | |
| Understand and use the vocabulary of estimation. | 9 | 9 | 9 | |
| Give a sensible estimate of a number of objects that can be checked by counting (up to about 30 objects). | 9 | 9 | 9 | |
| **Calculations** | | | | |
| *Understanding addition and subtraction* | | | | |
| **Understand the operation of addition and use the related vocabulary.** | 2, 7, 10 | 2, 7, 9, 13 | 10 | M |
| **Understand the operation of subtraction (as 'take away', 'difference' and 'how many more to make') and use the related vocabulary.** | 3,7 | 3, 7, 9, 13 | 3, 7, 10 | M |
| Begin to recognise that addition can be done in any order. | 2, 8, 10 | 9 | 10 | |
| Begin to use the +, – and = signs to record mental calculations in a number sentence, | 2, 3, 10 | 9, most | most | |
| and to recognise the use of symbols such as □ or △ to stand for an unknown number. | 2, 3, 5, 9 | 8, 9 | 3, 8 | |
| Begin to recognise that more than two numbers can be added together. | | | 2, 7, 10 | M3 |
| *Rapid recall of addition and subtraction facts* | | | | |
| **Know by heart: all pairs of numbers with a total of 10** (e.g. 3 + 7). | 10, 14 | 3 | 2 | M |
| addition facts for all pairs of numbers with a total up to at least 5, | 2, 7, 10, 14 | | | M |
| and the corresponding subtraction facts; | 3, 7, 10, 14 | | | M |
| addition doubles of all numbers to at least 5 (e.g. 4 + 4), | 8 | 10, 13 | 2 | M |
| Begin to know: addition facts for all pairs of numbers with a total up to at least 10, | 10, 14 | 3 | 3, 10 | M |
| and the corresponding subtraction facts. | | 3 | 3, 10 | M |
| *Mental calculation strategies (+ and –)* | | | | |
| Use knowledge that addition can be done in any order to do mental calculations more efficiently. For example: put the larger number first and count on in ones, including beyond 10 (e.g. 7 + 5). | 2 | 2 | | M2 M3 |
| Begin to partition into '5 and a bit' when adding 6, 7, 8 or 9, then recombine (e.g. 6 + 8 = 5 + 1 + 5 + 3 =10 + 4 = 14). | | 9 | 2 | |
| Identify near-doubles, using doubles already known (e.g. 6 + 5). | 10 | | | M3 |

Maths topics set in **bold type** in the main column are the **key objectives** given in the Mathematics Framework.
The numbers in the Term columns indicate the Unit where the objective is featured. 'most' indicates that the objective is being put into practice in most units. M indicates where the objective is practised in mental work in all three terms.
M2 or M3 indicates it is only in the later terms.

| | Term 1 | Term 2 | Term 3 | Mental |
|---|---|---|---|---|
| Add 9 to single-digit numbers by adding 10 then subtracting 1. | | | 2 | M3 |
| Use patterns of similar calculations (e.g. 10 − 0 = 10, 10 − 1 = 9, 10 − 2 = 8 ...). | 2, | 2, 3, 9 | 2 | |
| Use known number facts and place value to add or subtract a pair of numbers mentally within the range 0 to at least 10, then 0 to at least 20. | 10 | 3, 9 | 3, 10, 14 | M |
| Begin to bridge through 10, and later 20, when adding a single-digit number. | | | 10, 14 | |

## Solving problems

### Making decisions

| | Term 1 | Term 2 | Term 3 | Mental |
|---|---|---|---|---|
| Choose and use appropriate number operations and mental strategies to solve problems. | 4, 11 | 4, 10 | 4, 11 | |

### Reasoning about numbers or shapes

| | Term 1 | Term 2 | Term 3 | Mental |
|---|---|---|---|---|
| Solve simple mathematical problems or puzzles; recognise and predict from simple patterns and relationships. Suggest extensions by asking 'What if ...?' or 'What could I try next?' | 6, 7, 8, 14 | 6, 8 | 6, 8 | |
| Investigate a general statement about familiar numbers or shapes by finding examples that satisfy it. | 6, 8 | 8 | 6, 8, 14 | |
| Explain methods and reasoning orally. | 6, 7, 8 | 6, 8 | 6, 8 | |

### Problems involving 'real life', money or measures

| | Term 1 | Term 2 | Term 3 | Mental |
|---|---|---|---|---|
| **Use mental strategies to solve simple problems** set in 'real life', money, time or measurement contexts, **using counting, addition, halving or doubling, explaining methods and reasoning orally.** | 4, 5, 11, 12, 14 | 4, 5, 7, 10, 11, 13 | 4, 5, 11, 12 | |
| Recognise coins of different values; | 4, 11 | 4, 10 | 4, 7, 11 | |
| find totals and change from up to 20p; | 11 | 4, 10, 13 | 4, 7, 11, 14 | M |
| work out how to pay an exact sum using smaller coins. | 4 | 4, 7, 10 | 4, 11, 14 | |

### Organising and using data

| | Term 1 | Term 2 | Term 3 | Mental |
|---|---|---|---|---|
| Solve a given problem by sorting, classifying and organising information in simple ways, such as: using objects or pictures; in a list or simple table. Discuss and explain results. | 13 | 12 | 13 | |

## Measures, shape and space

### Measures

| | Term 1 | Term 2 | Term 3 | Mental |
|---|---|---|---|---|
| Understand and use the vocabulary related to length, mass and capacity. | 5, 7 | 5, 7 | 5, 7 | |
| **Compare two lengths, masses or capacities by direct comparison;** extend to more than two. | 5, 7 | 5 | 5 | |
| Measure using uniform non-standard units (e.g. straws, wooden cubes, plastic weights, yoghurt pots) or standard units (e.g. metre sticks, litre jugs). | 5 | 5, 7 | 5 | |
| **Suggest suitable standard or uniform non-standard units and measuring equipment to estimate, then measure, a length, mass or capacity,** | 5 | 5 | 5 | |
| recording estimates and measurements as 'about 3 beakers full' or 'about as heavy as 20 cubes'. | 5 | 5 | 5 | |
| Understand and use the vocabulary related to time. | 12 | 11 | 12 | |
| Order familiar events in time. | 12 | | 12 | |
| Know the days of the week and the seasons of the year. | 12 | 11 | 12 | M |
| Read the time to the hour or half hour on analogue clocks. | 12 | 11, 13 | 12, 14 | |

### Shape and space

| | Term 1 | Term 2 | Term 3 | Mental |
|---|---|---|---|---|
| **Use everyday language to describe features of familiar 3D and 2D shapes,** including the cube, cuboid, sphere, cylinder, cone ... circle, triangle, square, rectangle ... referring to properties such as the shapes of flat faces, or the number of faces or corners...or the number and types of sides. | 6, 7 | 6, 7 | | M |
| Make and describe models, patterns and pictures using construction kits, everyday materials, Plasticine..... | 6 | 6 | | |
| Fold shapes in half, then make them into symmetrical patterns. | | 6 | | |
| Begin to relate solid shapes to pictures of them. | 6 | 6 | | |
| Use everyday language to describe position, direction and movement. | | | 6, 7 | |
| Talk about things that turn. | | | 6 | |
| Make whole turns and half turns. | | | 6 | |
| Use one or more shapes to make, describe and continue repeating patterns. | | | 6, 7 | |

## Year 1 Term 2: Topic and Resources Planner

| Unit (days) | Framework for Teaching Mathematics • Topics | page numbers refer to this book | | | page numbers refer to other books | | |
|---|---|---|---|---|---|---|---|
| | | Lesson Plans | Copymasters | Homework Copymasters | Big Book | Shared Activity Book | Recording Book |
| **1** (2) | • Counting, properties of number and number sequences; Place value and ordering | *pages* 10–11 | – | – | *pages* 2–3 | *page* 2 | *pages* 2–3 |
| **2** (5) | • Place value and money<br>• Understanding addition and subtraction; Rapid recall of addition and subtraction facts; Mental calculation strategies (+ and –) | *pages* 12–13 | **1–2** *pages* 36–37 | **11–12** *pages* 46–47 | *pages* 4–5 | *page* 3 | *pages* 4–5 |
| **3** (5) | • Understanding addition and subtraction; Rapid recall; Mental calculation strategies (+ and –) | *pages* 14–15 | **3–5** *pages* 38–40 | **13** *page* 48 | *pages* 6–7 | *pages* 4–5 | *pages* 6–7 |
| **4** (5) | • Problems involving 'real life' or money; Making decisions | *pages* 16–17 | **6** *page* 41 | **14** *page* 49 | *pages* 8–9 | *page* 6 | *pages* 8–9 |
| **5** (5) | • Problems involving measures<br>• Measures | *pages* 18–19 | **7–8** *pages* 42–43 | **15** *page* 50 | *pages* 10–11 | *page* 7 | *pages* 10–11 |
| **6** (3) | • Reasoning about shapes<br>• Shape and space | *pages* 20–21 | – | **16** *page* 51 | *pages* 12–13 | *page* 8 | *pages* 12–13 |
| **7** (2) | *Assess and Review*<br>• Place value and ordering<br>• Understanding addition and subtraction<br>• Problems involving money<br>• Measures; Shape and space | *page* 21 | – | – | – | *page* 9 | *pages* 14–15 |
| **8** (5) | • Counting, properties of number and number sequences<br>• Reasoning about numbers | *pages* 22–23 | – | **17** *page* 52 | *pages* 14–15 | *page* 10 | *pages* 16–17 |
| **9** (5) | • Place value and ordering; Estimating<br>• Understanding addition and subtraction; Mental calculation strategies | *pages* 24–25 | – | **18** *page* 53 | *pages* 16–17 | *page* 11 | *pages* 18–20 |
| **10** (5) | • Problems involving 'real life' and money; Making decisions | *pages* 26–27 | – | **19** *page* 54 | *pages* 18–19 | *pages* 12–13 | *pages* 21–23 |
| **11** (5) | • Measures – time | *pages* 28–29 | – | **20** *page* 55 | *pages* 20–21 | *page* 14 | *pages* 24–27 |
| **12** (5) | • Organising and using data | *pages* 30–31 | **9–10** *pages* 44–45 | **21** *page* 56 | *pages* 22–23 | *page* 15 | *pages* 28–29 |
| **13** (2) | • Counting, properties of number and number sequences; Place value and ordering<br>• Understanding addition and subtraction; Rapid recall<br>• Making decisions; Problems involving money or time<br>• Measures – Time | *page* 32 | – | – | *page* 24 | *page* 16 | *pages* 30–31 |

## Non-print resources

| Teacher | Group | Pair | Individual child |
|---|---|---|---|
| large number cards, Blu-tack; large counters; number line | | a 1–6 dice; 2 counters | 20 Multilink blocks (or similar); number line |
| cards or counters with numbers 1–20; arrow cards, number line marked in tens from 0–100; classroom objects | counters; sorting toys | a 1–6 dice; 2 counters | number line; paper |
| number line | counters | 20 counters for activity; 2 dice (1–6) and 2 counters | number line |
| number line | coins; Plasticine 'biscuits', empty milk cartons, twists of paper 'sweets' (see Day 1); bricks | coins; 2 dice (1–6) and 12 counters in 2 colours; 2 dice (1–6) and 2 sheets of paper | cutlery (see Day 5) |
| deep and shallow balance scales; everyday objects for weighing (for details see pg 18) | 5/6 simple balance scales; everyday and classroom objects for weighing (for details see pg 18) | a two-toned counter or one marked *lighter* and *heavier*, 2 counters | sheet of paper |
| 3D shapes: cube, cuboid, sphere, cone, cylinder; 2D shapes: square, circle, triangle, rectangle; paper square; scissors | 3D shapes; construction kits; everyday materials; Plasticine | a 1–6 dice; 18 counters | number cards; scissors, a paper square, circle and rectangle |
| | 2D/3D shapes in bag; coins; 5 balance scales; 5 boxes marbles; 5 towers of Lego bricks | 2 sets of number cards 0–12; 18 counters; number line | number cards 0–20 |
| number cards 1–15 | Multilink; coloured pencils; counters; paper for recording sums | number cards 1–20; 2 dice (1–6) and 10 counters | |
| arrow cards; objects for estimating – beanbags, pencils, books, bag of sweets, Lego bricks; 6 large dominoes (5/0, 5/1, 5/2, 5/3, 5/4, 5/5); Blu-tack | sorting toys, counters, Multilink, marbles, beads, buttons, shells; set of dominoes | bag with number cards 8–16 and 16 counters in 2 colours (8 of each) | |
| | coins | coins including 2 × 1p, 2 × 2p, 2 × 5p, 2 × 10p; cloth bag; number cards 11–19; 1–6 dice; 1 real coin; 2 counters | number lines; number cards |
| 6 small clock faces, Blu-tack; geared clock; flashcards of days of week; simple one-minute timer; real clock | (see Day 5) choice of Lego, Multilink, beads and string, squared paper, Plasticine, jigsaws, bricks | coin; 2 counters; 2 clock faces | clock faces; number lines |
| 5 packets of crisps in different flavours/colours; sheets of paper; Blu-tack; 4 large sheets of card | bricks or Multilink; glue; one type per group of beads, counters, bricks, sorting toys | a 1–6 dice; 2 counters and access to the group's objects | scissors |
| geared clock | | a 1–6 dice and 2 counters | clock faces; number cards 0–9; number lines; 9 × 1p |

## Non-print resources planning overview

| General | NES-Arnold cat. no. × quantity to buy for 30 |
|---|---|
| Blu-tack or similar | eg SA640/8 ×1 |
| building kits i.e. LEGO | eg NB9438/8 ×1 |
| coloured pencils | eg F2233/6 ×1 |
| glue sticks | eg SA474/3 ×1 |
| gummed paper for 2D shapes | F785/2 ×1 |
| Plasticine | eg KC808/2 ×1 |
| squared paper | eg. DS100/20 ×1 |
| straws | F479/0 ×1 |
| **for teacher use** | |
| 2D shapes | eg NB1024/9 ×1+ |
| 3D shapes | eg NB6731/5 ×1+ |
| abacus | eg SX053/9 ×1 |
| class number line 0 to 20 | NB8509/6 ×1 |
| class washing line | NB7717/2 ×1 |
| flashcards, blank | NB7405/2 ×1 |
| floor tiles 0–9 | NB8459/2 ×1 |
| geared clock | eg NB8528/7 ×1 |
| large counters | 5KG372/0 ×1 |
| large dominoes | SX146/0 ×1 |
| large number cards 0–20 | eg. 8NB7717/2 ×1 |
| marbles | KN349/1 ×1 |
| number line 0–100 | 8NB8509/6 ×1 |
| number stick | SY040/6 ×1 |
| place value cards | 8NB8945/8 ×1 |
| quartz timer | 5SY390/8 ×1 |
| real clock | 5NB9328/2 ×1 |
| soft foam ball | eg L9739/2 ×1 |
| stopwatch or timer | eg NB8530/0 ×1 |
| **for group/pair use** | |
| balance scales | SX271/5 ×15 |
| beads | NB8983/0 ×2 |
| beanbags | L3062/98 ×1 |
| blank dice | SX184/2 ×6 |
| buttons | 5NB1122/2 ×1 |
| counters | KG370/4 ×1 |
| dice 0–5 | NB9746/6 ×6 |
| dice 1–6 | SX100/4 ×6 |
| dominoes | 5SX146/0 ×8 |
| feely bags | NB9842/3 ×3 |
| Multilink | NB6679/8 ×1 |
| set of mixed coins to £1 | NB1580/4 ×3 |
| £2 coins | NB8848/8 ×1 |
| extra 1p, | NB1571/0 ×2 |
| 2p, | NB1572/3 ×1 |
| 5p | NB1573/6 ×1 |
| sorting dishes | NB1347/9 ×2 |
| sorting toys | eg NB5137/6 ×1 |
| **for individual use** | |
| cards 0–20 | NB9734/3 ×3 |
| clock faces | eg NB7583/1 ×3 |
| cutlery | NB5040/3 ×1 |
| desk number line 0–20 | NB8950/0 ×3 |
| number line 0–100 | 8NB8949/0 ×3 |
| scissors | eg NB7063/2 ×3 |
| **suggested storage** | |
| individual zip wallet | eg KK6790/0 ×2 |

We recommend that every child keeps their number cards in a zip wallet KK6790/0 or other small storage box. The optimum way to store pair and group activity items (Multilink cubes, coins, dice, etc.) is in one box or zip wallet per table, each box / wallet holding sufficient for all the children.

NES-Arnold provides a dedicated order form for these and other resources suggested for use in conjunction with the Oxford Maths Zone. For a copy, please phone NES-Arnold on 0115 936 0223 or fax 0115 945 2326

Oxford Maths Zone software is also available. There is a CD-ROM for each year. The disc for Year 1 covers counting, place value, addition and subtraction. For more details contact the Oxford Numeracy Care-line or 01865 267241.

**YEAR 1 | TERM 2**

# Unit 1

**Number:** Counting, properties of number and number sequences; Place value and ordering

Vocabulary: odd; even; every other number; sixty; seventy; eighty; ninety; hundred

Resources: *Teacher* large number cards; Blu-tack; large counters; number line; *Pair* a 1–6 dice; 2 counters; *Child* 20 Multilink blocks (or similar); number line

**DAY 1**

*Count on and back in ones from any small number (to 20); Order numbers to at least 20 and position them on a number line*

## Mental

Clap and Count: to 30
Before and After: one before / after any given number to 20

## Main Session

• **Counting on and back in ones: Big Book page 2.** The children are at the swimming pool: discuss what is happening at the desk. Ask children to read aloud the numbers on the key-board, starting with one. *The first key is on one, on which number is the next key? Count on from 4, from 7, etc. Count back from 7, 16, etc.* Extend to 30 if appropriate.

• **Ordering numbers to 20.** Ask children to Blu-tack a set of large number cards to the wall, in order from 0–20, making a number line. Children use the number

line to answer questions, e.g. *Count on from 5, back from 17. Which number comes before 11? after 15? Count back three from 12. Which number did you land on? Count on 5 from 0.* Remove the number line and repeat the activity.

• **Counting on and back in ones: Shared Activity Book page 2.** Each pair needs a 1–6 dice and 2 counters. *Take turns to throw the dice. Move your counter forward the number of spaces shown on the dice. If you land on a swimmer, throw the dice again and move your counter back that number of spaces. Who is first to reach the steps?*

## Plenary

*Did you land on a swimmer, Joe? Which one? How many did you count back from there? Which number did Joe have to move back to?*

**Key idea.** When we count every number we are counting in ones.

Big Book p.2

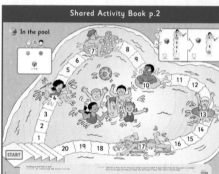
Shared Activity Book p.2

**DAY 2**

*Count on in twos from zero, then one, and begin to recognise odd or even numbers to about 20 as 'every other number'*

## Mental

Names and Numbers: numerals and names to 20
Before and After: one before / after any given number to 20

## Main Session

• **Counting on in twos: Big Book page 2.** *How are the children lined up?* (in twos) *Count the children in twos... 2, 4, 6, 8. Why would we count in twos?* (quicker) Ask 8 children to line up in front of the class. *Count the children one by one...1, 2...* Line the children up in twos. *Now count in twos...2, 4, 6, 8. Did we get the same answer both times? When would we count in twos?* Discuss. (children in a line, sharing sweets, going up stairs, etc.)

• **Counting on and back in twos.** Take 10 large counters and Blu-tack them on the board in twos. *Count them in twos...2, 4... And back again... We have 10, count back 2 leaves 8, 6....* Put one counter back in the box and ask a child to line the rest up in twos. *What happens? There is an odd one out.* Discuss *odd* and

*even. When we count in twos from zero, we are saying only the even numbers. Every other number is an odd number.* Demonstrate on a number line. *When we count on in twos from 1 we are saying the odd numbers and this time every other number is an even number.*

• **Odd and even numbers: Big Book page 3.** *Why is the little boy worried?* (he can't find his locker) *Which number is his locker?* (9) *Why couldn't he find it in front of him?* Establish that the lockers are divided into odd and even numbers. *Read the odd numbers. Read the even numbers.* Write *odd* and *even* on the board. *Mo has key number 2. Is that an odd or an even number?* Repeat for Jim and Max. *If you had an odd-numbered key between 9 and 13 which number would it be?* etc.

• **Odd and even numbers: Recording Book page 2.** *Count the number of objects in each group and draw a line to match them to the correct number. Then colour the odd number boxes blue and the even number boxes yellow.* If children need help, encourage them to join objects in 2s.

## Plenary

Discuss the Recording Book. *How many goggles were there?* (17) *Is that an odd or an even number? How do we know when a number is an odd or an even number?*

**Key idea.** When we count every other number, we are counting in twos.

Big Book p.3

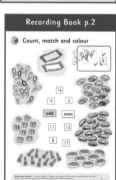
Recording Book p.2

## DAY 3

*Count reliably at least 20 objects; Count on in twos from one; Count in tens from and back to zero*

## Mental

Washing Line: ordering numbers 0–20
Bigger and Smaller: to 20

## Main Session

• **Counting reliably.** Multilink or similar. Children each take 20 pieces. Partner counts to check. *Count in twos from zero...0, 2, 4,* etc. *Now you have a pile of 20, count back in twos from 20.*

• **Counting in tens.** *Push the Multilink together in rods of ten. Count your rods and your partner's. 10, 20, 30, 40. Which tens number comes next?* Extend the counting in tens to 100. Write the numerals on the board in a column so that children can see the pattern. Ask 5 children each to bring out 2 rods of ten. *Count as*

they hold them up...10, 20, ...100 and back again. What does 60 mean? (6 tens) Demonstrate with 6 rods of ten. Repeat for 70 to 100. *Which tens number comes between 50 and 70? after 90? before 20?*

• **Counting on in twos from one.** Number lines. *Start at 1 and count on 2. Which number comes next? and then?* Continue until 19 is reached then count back to 1. *Are these odd or even numbers? Start at 7 and count on in twos. Start at 15 and count back in twos.*

• **Counting in tens and twos: Recording Book page 3.** *Fill in the missing numbers on the number lines and in the boxes.*

## Plenary

Discuss the Recording Book page. *2, 4, 6 which number came next? 15,13,11 then? Is ten an even number? How do you know?*

**Key idea.** When we count in tens we add on ten each time.

**Recording Book p.3**

Count in 10s and 2s

60, 70, 80, ☐ . ☐     90, 80, 70, ☐ . ☐
50, 40, 30, ☐ . ☐     10, 20, 30, ☐ . ☐

2, 4, 6, ☐ . ☐     20, 18, 16, ☐ . ☐
1, 3, 5, ☐ . ☐     15, 13, 11, ☐ . ☐

## Other Copymasters

The Copymasters shown here are for general use throughout the term. Copymaster 11 introduces for parents the role of the homework sheets and may be used as often as appropriate. The Number Card Copymasters (22&23) are identical in size to those which can be purchased from NES-Arnold as catalogue

number NB 8941/6 in laminated, round-cornered format. The Arrow Card Copymaster (24) is larger than those available from NES-Arnold, being intended for class demonstration only. Copymaster 25 is a class record sheet which links directly to the individual records made on the back of the *Recording Book.*

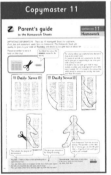

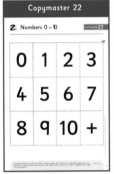

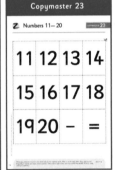

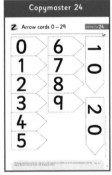

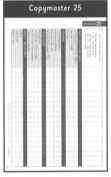

# Unit 2

**Number:** Place value and ordering
**Calculations:** Understanding addition and subtraction; Rapid recall of addition and subtraction facts; Mental calculation strategies (+ and −)

**Vocabulary:** one more / less than; one after / before; units; tens; sum; total; add; addition; count on; altogether; take away; count back; subtract

**Resources:** *Teacher* cards or counters with numbers 1–20; arrow cards, number line marked in tens from 0 to 100; classroom objects to demonstrate addition; *Group* counters; sorting toys; *Pair* a 1–6 dice; 2 counters; *Child* number line; paper

---

### DAY 1

*Within the range 0 to 30, say the number that is 1 more or less than any given number*

## Mental

Counting Hat: counting on in twos
Bigger and Smaller: to 30

## Main Session

• **One more / less: Big Book pages 4&5.** Compare the two pictures. *Is there **one more / one less** of anything? Look at the border. Read these numbers. (1–6) What is one more than 6? What is one less than 13? Count on in ones from 6 (to 16). What number is one after 16? What number is hidden behind the cricket bat? How will we work out what number is hidden behind the yellow bag?* (one more than 18 / one less than 20) (Extension: include numbers beyond 20.)

• **One more / less; guess the number.** Cards or bag of counters each with a number (1 to 20). Child picks one (unseen) and makes up a question, e.g. *This number is one after 16.* Encourage them to vary the vocabulary used. *Say it another way.*

• **Bingo: Copymaster 1.** Call out *one after 13 / one less than 12,* etc. Children work out the answers and cross them off on their cards. (N.B. Keep a note of your answers to verify the winners' cards.)

## Plenary

Discuss the Bingo game. *Which number did you have left? What question might be asked for you to cross off that number?*

**Key idea.** To find one **more** we **add** one to the number.

Big Book pages 4&5

Bedtime (1)    Bedtime (2)

Copymaster 1

Bingo cards

| 10 | 7 | 20 | | 13 | 6 | 5 |
| 19 | 2 | 17 | | 8 | 11 | 4 |

| 20 | 5 | 3 | | 9 | 1 | 13 |
| 12 | 16 | 14 | | 7 | 12 | 15 |

| 19 | 15 | 17 | | 2 | 16 | 13 |
| 3 | 10 | 6 | | 7 | 19 | 8 |

| 18 | 4 | 15 | | 11 | 9 | 17 |
| 6 | 20 | 9 | | 1 | 12 | 18 |

---

### DAY 2

*Begin to know what each number in a two-digit number represents; Within the range 0 to 30, say the number that is 10 more or less than any given number*

## Mental

Counting Stick: counting on and back in tens to 100
Card Game: addition bonds of 5

## Main Session

• **Tens and ones; ten more / less: Big Book page 4.** *Eva is teaching her little brother a nursery rhyme.* (Ten little fingers and ten little toes, two little ears and one little nose, two little eyes that shut so tight, and one little mouth to kiss Teddy 'Goodnight'.) *How many fingers is Eva holding up? How many is her little brother holding up? What is ten more than eight?* Use arrow cards to demonstrate. (Hold up a 1 ten arrow card and an 8 to read 18.) *Ten more than four? Ten less than sixteen?* Ask similar questions using numbers to 20.

• **Ten more / less; number line game.** Count together in tens to 100. Display a number line marked only in tens from 0 to 100. Choose a number and emphasise the start, e.g. *sixty. How many tens make **sixty**? What number is ten more than **sixty**?* Repeat with a few tens numbers to 100 then play the game. Divide class into 4 teams. A player from each team comes forward and sits at the front. Ask a question (*ten more / less than*) and players stand up when the answer is known. First to stand up is allowed to go to the number line and point to the answer. If correct they score a point for the team. Then the next 4 come forward.

• **1 or 10 more / less than: Recording Book page 4.** Revise the reading of the words *more / less than*. *At the top of the page, count one more than or one less than. At the bottom of the page, count ten more than or ten less than.*

## Plenary

Relate the *more / less than* questions to money, e.g. *A toy car costs 40p. A truck costs 10p more. How do we work out the cost of a truck? A can of juice costs 30p. A small carton costs 10p less. How do we work out the cost of a carton?*

**Key idea.** To find ten **less** we **take** 10 **away** from the number.

Recording Book p.4

More than, less than

## DAY 3

*Understand the operation of addition and use the related vocabulary; Put the larger number first and count on in ones; Understand and use the vocabulary of comparing numbers*

### Mental

Counting Hat: counting on in twos from 1
Ball Game Doubles: doubling numbers to 5

### Main Session

- **Combination of 2 sets: Big Book page 5.** *Look at the shelves. How many aeroplanes are there? How many cars? How many toys altogether? What kind of sum did you do?...* **You added the 2 sets of toys to find the total number.** Demonstrate with classroom objects to reinforce this type of addition. (*7 red pencils and 2 blue ones, how many altogether?* etc.) Vary the vocabulary used.

- **Putting the larger number first; comparing numbers.** Ask a child to demonstrate by using a number line. *Point to 4. Add on 3. What is the answer? You can add by counting on along a number line. Put the larger number first then count on. Add 2 and 6. Which number is larger?* Demonstrate on the number line. Invite children to make up 'story sums' based on the Big Book picture. Another demonstrates the procedure on the number line.
- **Addition practice: Recording Book page 5.** Counters. *Write the answers in the boxes. Use counters or the number line if you need help.*

### Plenary

*If you do an addition sum, will your answer be more than or less than the numbers with which you started?*
**Key idea.** Addition means adding numbers together to find the total.

Recording Book p.5

## DAY 4

**Use patterns of similar calculations**

### Mental

Thumbs Up, Thumbs Down: for odd and even numbers
Fast Facts to Five: facts to 5

### Main Session

- **Number patterns: Big Book page 5.** *How many cars are on the floor? How many on the shelf? How many altogether?* Write $2 + 4 = 6$ on the board. Set out toy cars to demonstrate $2 + 4 = 6$. *Who can use the cars to make a different pattern for 6?* As children suggest and show their answers, write the combinations on the board in sequence, to show the pattern of the numbers. Discuss the pattern and relationship of the numbers.
- **Using a number pattern.** Write up the first 3 facts of the addition pattern of 7, starting with $0 + 7 = 7$.

*Look at the pattern and use it to work out what number sentence comes next. Four and what number would make 7? How can we work it out using the pattern?* Complete the addition pattern for 7.
- **Making a number pattern.** Counters / sorting toys, paper. Children choose a number from 4 to 10 for themselves. (You may wish to direct the less able to a low number.) Each child writes down the addition pattern of the number sentences, starting with $0 +$ (the number). They may use counters or sorting toys to lay out the pattern before writing it. Display the patterns.

### Plenary

Discuss the patterns. *Are these patterns of 6 the same?* Cover part of a pattern. *What comes next? How did you work it out?*
**Key idea.** We can use a number pattern to help us work out an answer to a number question.

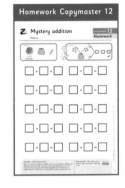

Homework Copymaster 12

## DAY 5

*Know by heart addition and subtraction facts for all numbers to 7*

### Mental

Ball Game Twos: counting on and back in twos from 0 or 1
Thumbs Up, Thumbs Down: for odd and even numbers

### Main Session

- **Facts to 5.** Do a quick revision of the known facts to 5 by having a quiz or playing one of the mental games such as Fast Facts to Five.
- **Facts to 7.** *Yesterday we worked out the number pattern for the facts of 6. Who can remember a fact of 6?* Write the facts on the board as the children volunteer them. Repeat for 7. With the facts still displayed, have children take turns to be the 'teacher' and ask questions of the others. Then hide the facts.

- **Addition and subtraction facts to 7: Shared Activity Book page 3** with **Copymaster 2.** Each pair needs 2 counters, 1 dice and a strip of sums from the Copymaster. *Player 1 chooses a sum from the strip and reads it (but not the answer) to player 2. If the answer is correct, player 2 throws the dice and moves up the board. If not correct they miss a turn. Who is first to reach the toy box?* Vary by using a more difficult set of sums.

### Plenary

Discuss the game. *Who won? What helped you to answer quickly? Was there a fact you did not know?*
**Key idea.** Learning number facts by heart helps me to work faster.

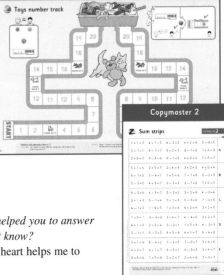

Shared Activity Book p.3

Copymaster 2

Calculations: **Understanding addition and subtraction; Rapid recall; Mental calculation strategies (+ and –)**

Vocabulary: subtract; take away; difference; pattern; number facts

Resources: *Teacher* number line; *Group* counters; *Pair* 20 counters for activity; 2 dice (1–6) and 2 counters; *Child* number line

---

## DAY 1

### *Understand the operation of subtraction as 'take away'*

### Mental

Five Fingers: subtraction within 5 – emphasis on vocabulary

Arrow Card Game: 'teens' numbers 11 to 19

### Main Session

• **Understanding subtraction as 'take away': Big Book pages 6&7.** *How many little lambs are in the first picture? How many are left in the pen in the second picture? So how many have escaped? How did you do it?* (take away, subtract) *There are 10 hens in the yard on page 6 and 4 on page 7. How many less than 10 is 4? What kind of sum is this?* Demonstrate how counters may be used to work out the answer. *Lay out the larger number and subtract the smaller number from the larger.*

• **Taking away.** Counters. Each child lays out counters in response to questions such as *8 take away 4 leaves...*

and holds up a number card to show the answer. Once the children are confident about laying out the larger number and subtracting the smaller, vary the questioning to include *Take 6 away from 8. How many are left?* With the children, write up some of the subtractions on the board using the – and = signs.

• **Counting back.** Use the number line and ask questions using the subtraction vocabulary *subtract, take away, how many less than, how many are left?* Invite children to be 'teacher' and ask some questions of their own.

### Plenary

*How do we subtract 2 numbers? find how many less than...? take away?*

**Key idea.** To subtract we can take the smaller number away from the larger number to find how many are left.

Big Book pages 6&7

---

## DAY 2

### *Understand the operation of subtraction as 'difference'*

### Mental

Tricky Sixes: addition and subtraction facts of 6
Bigger and Smaller: to 30

### Main Session

• **Difference between: Big Book pages 6&7.** *Count the ducks to find how many are in each picture. What is the difference between the number of ducks in the first picture and the number of ducks in the second picture?* Discuss how it was calculated. Ask a few more questions using the Big Book or classroom objects as visual aids.

• **Finding the difference.** Play with a partner. Each takes a number of counters from the box (between 1 to 10, or adjust according to ability). The children then count both piles and *find the difference between the*

*numbers.* This can be done by matching the counters, or mentally by taking the smaller number from the larger.

• **Finding the difference between 2 numbers: Shared Activity Book page 4.** Each pair needs 2 dice (1–6). *Take turns to throw both dice and find the difference between the 2 numbers. Your partner checks that the answer is correct, then you move forward that number of spaces. Who is first to reach the barn?*

### Plenary

*How do we find the difference between 2 numbers?*

**Key idea.** To find the difference between 2 numbers, we can take the smaller number away from the larger, or count on from the smaller number to the larger.

Shared Activity Book p.4

---

## DAY 3

### *Understand the operation of subtraction and use the related vocabulary*

### Mental

Ball Game Twos: counting back in twos from 21
Arrow Card Game: 'teens' numbers 11 to 19

### Main Session

• **Subtraction practice: Copymaster 3.** *I will give you a subtraction sum. You work out the answer in your head, with counters or on the number line. Then colour in the section on your sheet which has the same number.* Ask questions using the known subtraction vocabulary, avoiding questions with the answers 5, 8, 9 or 10.

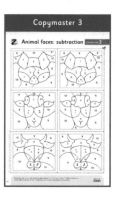

Copymaster 3

All cards have the same numbers but in different arrangements to prevent 'copying', and when completed correctly should reveal an animal face.
• **Written subtraction practice: Recording Book page 6.** Counters. *Write the answer to each sum in the box beside it. Use counters or the number line.*

## Plenary

Discuss the activities. *How did you work out the answer… in your head, with counters? Show us how the answer could be worked out using a number line. Was your answer more than or less than the larger number in the question?*
**Key idea.** When we subtract we are left with a smaller number.

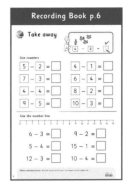

Recording Book p.6

---

# DAY 4

## Use patterns of similar calculations

### Mental

Five Fingers: subtraction within 5 – emphasis on vocabulary
Guess the Number: find the number between two others

### Main Session

• **Making patterns of similar calculations: Big Book page 6.** *There are 8 lambs in the pen and 2 mother sheep. How many lambs could each mother have?* List the combinations on the board, writing each fact in its sequential order so the pattern of addition facts to 8 emerges. Continue until all the addition facts for 8 are listed, encouraging the children to use the pattern to fill in any blank spaces. Read the list aloud together. *What patterns do you see?* Emphasise the vertical patterns. *We can make subtraction sums, using the same numbers and the minus sign. Look at the list and help me make the subtraction facts for 8. Start with 8 – 0 = ?*
• **Number facts to 9.** *We have listed the addition facts and the subtraction facts for 8. Help me write the facts for 9.* List the numbers from 0 to 9 in a column, encouraging the children to help by calling out the next number. Then write +9, +8 , etc. and finish with the answer column = 9. Using the visual display, all repeat the number 'stories' aloud. Rub out the last 3 rows and ask *What is 8 + 1? How did you know?*
• **Using patterns of similar calculations: Recording Book page 7.** *Look carefully at each list and fill in the missing numbers to complete the pattern.*

### Plenary

Discuss the Recording Book page. *How did you know which number to fill in? Tell me about the pattern.*
**Key idea.** Number patterns can help us work out the answers to addition and subtraction sums.

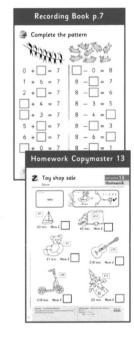

Recording Book p.7

Homework Copymaster 13

---

# DAY 5

## Begin to know addition facts for all pairs of numbers with a total up to 10, and the corresponding subtraction facts; Use known number facts and place value to add or subtract a pair of numbers mentally (range 0–10)

### Mental

Tricky Sixes: addition and subtraction facts of 6
Washing Line: ordering numbers 20–0

### Main Session

• **Facts for 8 and 9.** Display the lists made yesterday for 9 and 8. Read the facts together. Ask questions, encouraging quick responses. Finish with 4 + 4.
• **Facts for 10.** Ask for facts of 10 which are already known. *A double for 10? One less than 10?* As the facts are volunteered, list them on the board in order and encourage children to suggest the missing facts. Read the completed list and ask a few questions to enable children to begin to learn the facts.

• **Using known number facts to add or subtract mentally: Shared Activity Book page 5** with **Copymasters 4&5.** Photocopy the Copymasters back to back and laminate if possible before cutting into 2 sets of 8 cards. Each child is given one set of cards. *Lay out your cards with the numbers facing up. Place the card with the correct answer over the sum on the board. When all the cards are in place, turn them over to see the picture.* (The sets of cards have the same numbers, but each board has a different set of questions. The children could change places and play another game.)

### Plenary

Discuss the game. *Who finished first? Why was that? What would help you to answer quickly?*
**Key idea.** Knowing the number facts helps me to answer quickly.

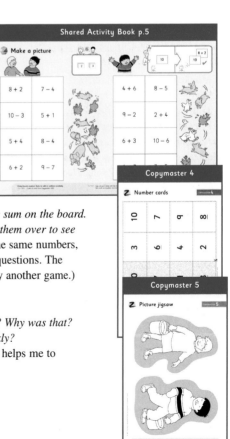

Shared Activity Book p.5

Copymaster 4

Copymaster 5

# Unit 4

**Sol Pr:** Problems involving 'real life' or money; Making decisions

Vocabulary: worth the same as; change; how much altogether; cost; spend; problem; think; decide; choose then work it out; total; difference

Resources: *Teacher* number line; *Group* coins; Plasticine 'biscuits', empty milk cartons, twists of paper 'sweets' (see Day 1); bricks; *Pair* coins; 2 dice (1–6) and 12 counters in 2 colours; 2 dice (1–6) and 2 sheets of paper; *Child* cutlery (see Day 5)

---

**DAY 1**

Recognise coins of different values; Find totals and change from up to 20p

## Mental

Counting Stick: counting on and back in tens
Speedy Sixes and Sevens: addition and subtraction facts of 6 and 7

## Main Session

• **Recognising coins.** Ask questions – children hold up the appropriate coin to answer, e.g. *Who can show me a 2p? Which coin is worth the same as five pennies? This coin is worth two five pences, what is it?* etc.

• **Using coins to make totals: Big Book pages 8&9.** Discuss the picture. *Steve has a carton of milk on his tray. How much does the milk cost? Which coins could we use to buy a carton of milk? Salma has a round biscuit on her tray. How much does it cost? Which coins could we use to make 12p? Which coin has fallen in Steve's custard? How many £1 coins are worth the same amount? Can you think of another way to make £2.00?*

• **Finding totals and giving change.** Children work in groups to practise buying items and giving change from amounts up to 20p. One is the shopkeeper who sells Plasticine 'biscuits' at 10p, 12p and 18p, (empty) cartons of milk at 6p, and paper twist 'sweets' at 5p. Use the Big Book for the price list. Each customer has one each of 1p, 2p, 5p, 10p and 20p coins to spend in the shop.

• **Finding totals: Recording Book page 8.** *Add the prices together to find the total cost. Write your answer in the box.*

## Plenary

Discuss the shop play. *What did you buy with your money? Which coins did you use to pay? How did you give 9p change?*
**Key idea.** To find the total cost add the prices together.

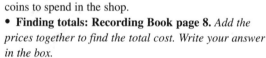

Big Book pages 8&9

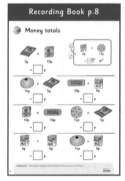

Recording Book p.8

---

**DAY 2**

Find totals and change from up to 20p

## Mental

Card Game: addition bonds of 7
In My Pocket: money problems within 6p

## Main Session

• **Giving change.** Ask children to demonstrate, on a number line, the answers to a few questions such as *20 take away 4, subtract 7 from 18*, then use a money context. *You have 20p and spend 13p. You need 7p change. How could you give 7p change?* Discuss and establish that they could count on from 13p in ones... 13p, ...20p, or they could work out how to make 7p (3 × 2p + 1p, 5p + 2p, etc.).

• **Practical.** Use the shop items from yesterday. This time the children work in pairs and take turns to be the shopkeeper. The customers may only use 10p and 20p coins to pay.

• **Giving change: Copymaster 6.** The Copymaster has a number line to help with subtraction. Children may choose to give change all in pennies or in combinations of coins. You decide whether you want them to lay out or draw round the coins. *Each time give change from 20p by laying coins on the sheet. Draw round each coin and write the value inside it. In the box, write how much change you are giving.*

## Plenary

Discuss the Copymaster. *How did you give 9p change? Did anyone do it another way? Are both ways correct?*
**Key idea.** To find how much change to give, find the difference between the cost and the money the customer gives.

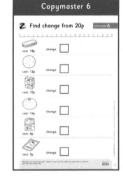

Copymaster 6

---

**DAY 3**

Choose and use appropriate number operations and mental strategies to solve problems

## Mental

Days of the Week 1: sequence of days
Number Cards: addition and subtraction facts to 7

## Main Session

• **Revise:** the steps **think about the problem**, **decide which kind of sum** you need to do, **choose how you will do the sum**, then **work it out**. Work out a few examples together to demonstrate, e.g. *The cook bought 9 bags of potatoes this week. She used 7 of them. How many are left?* Establish a variety of ways to work – mentally, draw a diagram, use apparatus.

- **Add or subtract: Shared Activity Book page 6.** Each pair needs 2 dice (1–6) and 12 counters in 2 colours. *Each uses a different colour of counter. Take turns to throw both dice. Choose whether to add or subtract to make the number for one of the foods. Place a counter on the food if you can make the number (partner checks). Who has the funniest lunch?*
- **Deciding and choosing.** Have bricks available if requested. *Decide which kind of sum you need to do, choose how you will solve the problem.* Set the problem: *The cook has tins stacked in 2 rows on the shelf. Each row has one tin less than the row beneath. The top row has 3 tins. How many tins are there altogether?*

## Plenary

Discuss the problem. *Why did you do it that way?*
**Key idea.** To solve a problem I choose which kind of sum to do and decide how to work it out.

Shared Activity Book p.6

---

*Use mental strategies to solve simple problems set in 'real life' or money contexts, using counting, addition or subtraction, explaining methods and reasoning orally*

## Mental

In My Pocket: money problems within 7p
Speedy Sixes and Sevens: addition and subtraction facts of 6 and 7

## Main Session

- **Understanding problems.** Remind children that they must think about the problem, decide which kind of sum to do and choose how to work. Then they work out the answer. *Max has 3 coins in his pocket. Together they make 12p. Which coins does he have?* Have coins available for children to use, but do not suggest they must use them. Allow time to work then discuss the solution together. (Answer: 10p + 1p + 1p or 5p + 5p + 2p.) *Two different answers, are they both correct? How can we find out?* Establish that sometimes there is more than one way of solving a problem.

- **Developing a strategy: Big Book page 9.** Look at the price list. *Salma gave the assistant a 10p coin and was given 4p change. What did she buy?* Allow time to think then discuss **how** to work it out. *What kind of sum will you do?* Discuss. Use a wrong answer to show that a problem may not be solved at the first attempt, so we try again. *How do we know when we have the correct answer?* We check the question to find out if the answer fits. Demonstrate. Establish that one way of solving a problem is to try a number and check to see if it works.
- **Using own strategies: Recording Book page 9.** Work with the children to solve the first problem, then leave them to work unaided. *What kind of sum should we do to work out how much is hidden? Write the answers in the boxes.*

## Plenary

Discuss the Recording Book page and the solution(s) to the problems.
**Key idea.** There may be more than one correct answer to a problem. ▌

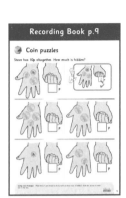

Recording Book p.9

Coin puzzles

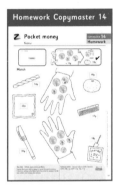

Homework Copymaster 14

Pocket money

---

Choose and use appropriate number operations and mental strategies to solve problems

## Mental

Number Line Race: ten more / less than
Ball Game Twos: counting in twos to 30

## Main Session

- **Drawing a diagram or using apparatus.** *A cook has arranged some jellies on a tray. There are 3 more orange jellies than red ones and there are 2 more red jellies than green ones. There are 2 green jellies. How many jellies are there altogether?* Discuss the problem and work it out together. *Start with what we know.* Use counters and draw diagrams on the board to demonstrate different ways of working then ask children to **decide** whether to find the final answer by adding or counting.
- **Drawing / using apparatus.** *Some cutlery has been laid out in a long line. Knife, fork, spoon, knife, fork, spoon and so on. What will be number 12 in the line?* Discuss and draw, or use cutlery to work out the answer.
- **Number puzzle.** Work in pairs with 2 dice (1–6), sheet of paper each. Look again at **Shared Activity Book page 6.** *When you played the game you had to throw 2 dice. You added or subtracted the numbers you threw to make one of the numbers on the foods. How could you make 12?* Discuss – only one way. *How many different ways can you make the number 4 by adding or by subtracting the numbers on two dice?* Record by drawing spots or writing the numbers.

## Plenary

Display and discuss the solutions to the number puzzle. *How many ways did you make 4?*
**Key idea.** The answer to a problem can sometimes be worked out by drawing or by using objects.

**Sol Pr:** **Problems involving measures**
**M Sh Sp:** **Measures**

*Vocabulary:* heavy; light; heavier; lighter; heaviest; lightest; weighs; balances; guess... roughly; nearly; about the same as; enough; not enough

*Resources:* *Teacher* large packet of Cornflakes and small porridge oats, crisps and nuts – or similar; feather and ball; banana, 2p coin and apple; button, book and sweet; comb and tin of pet food; mushroom and orange; fork, leaf and spoon (see Recording Book page 10); deep and shallow balance scales; *Group* 5 or 6 sets of simple balance scales; Day 1: fruit, vegetables or classroom objects for comparing or weighing; Day 2: cards and fruit / vegetables; Day 3: 5 apples, 5 small turnips, 5 oranges, 5 carrots and units for measuring, Plasticine; Day 4: small cubes, beanbags, straws, a sock, tin of dog food, spoon, tube of sweets, letter and house brick; Day 5: cards and fruit / vegetables; *Pair* a two-toned counter or one marked *lighter* and *heavier*; 2 counters; *Child* sheet of paper

---

**DAY 1**

Understand and use the vocabulary related to mass; *Compare two masses by direct comparison*

## Mental

Bigger and Smaller: for tens numbers 10–100
Double Dare: doubling numbers 1–6

## Main Session

• **Weight vocabulary: Big Book pages 10&11.**
Discuss the picture. Establish the need for food to be weighed so that each creature receives its share. Discuss the zoo animals, using the vocabulary *heavy, light, heavier, lighter, weighs, about the same as.* Use flashcards to teach the reading of the key words, *heavier, lighter, heaviest, lightest, about the same as.*
• **Comparing mass.** Pieces of fruit. *Which is heavier, the apple or the banana?* Repeat with other fruit. Use *lighter, about the same, balances.*
Divide class into two groups. Group 1 do Activity 1 while the rest go round the 'stations' to measure. Change round so that all tackle both activities.
• **Activity 1. Using vocabulary: Shared Activity**

**Book page 7.** Each pair needs a two-toned counter or one marked *lighter* and *heavier* and 2 counters. The children have to decide whether the adjacent square represents something lighter or heavier than where they are currently.
• **Activity 2. Comparing mass.**
5 or 6 sets of simple balance scales. Children work in twos or threes. At each 'station' have 2 objects (fruit, vegetables, classroom objects). Find which is heavier / lighter by comparing then weighing.

## Plenary

Discuss the weighing activity. *Which weighed heavier, the potato or the carrot? How did you find out? Were you always correct? Why not?*
**Key idea.** We work out whether one thing is heavier or lighter than another by comparing them both.

Big Book pages 10&11

Shared Activity Book p.7

---

**DAY 2**

*Compare two masses by direct comparison, extend to more than two; Record; Solve simple practical problems*

## Mental

Card Game: addition bonds of 8
Days of the Week 1: day before / after

## Main Session

• **Comparing mass: Big Book page 11.** *Look at the elephants. Which weighs more, the mother or the baby?* Repeat with zookeeper and Anna, etc. *Will a larger object always weigh heavier than a smaller one?* Use objects to demonstrate, e.g. large pack of Cornflakes / small pack of porridge oats; packets of crisps / nuts. Establish the need to weigh objects to ensure accuracy. Use 2 potatoes. *Make a 'good guess'* as to which is lighter. Compare, then use scales to check. Add a third potato. *Which is lightest?* Discuss how it could be done by elimination. Place the potatoes in order. Use *'good guess', roughly, nearly, about the same as, light, lighter, lightest.*

Half do Activity 1, the rest work in twos or threes to do Activity 2, then change round.
• **Activity 1. Comparing mass: Recording Book page 10.** Lay objects out at the side of the room so that children can check later. *Draw a line to match an object to each label. Use the real objects to check if necessary.*
• **Activity 2. Comparing by weighing.** A card with the question on it, fruit / vegetables and a set of simple balance scales at each station. Issue pieces of paper so that children can draw to record their 'good guess', and tick it if correct. Substitute fruit / vegetables as available, e.g. station 1: tomato, tangerine *Which is heavier?* 2: carrot, apple *Which is lighter?*
At the end of the session have some children check the answers to Activity 1 by weighing the objects.

## Plenary

Discuss the activities. *Was it always easy to tell which was heavier?*
**Key idea.** We can tell whether things are heavier or lighter by balancing them on the scales.

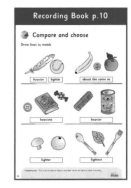

Recording Book p.10

## DAY 3

Measure using uniform non-standard or standard units; *Suggest suitable units to estimate then measure mass, recording estimates and measurements*

### Mental

Speedy Sixes and Sevens: addition and subtraction facts of 6 and 7
Counting Hat: counting on in twos from 0 or 1

### Main Session

• **Using units to measure.** *How could I sort a bag of potatoes in order from heaviest to lightest?* Lead children to suggest using units of measure. Accept all reasonable suggestions (e.g. marbles, cubes, beads, etc.). Weigh and order 5 potatoes, using the vocabulary: *'good guess', nearly, balances, enough.*
Half the class do Activity 1. The rest work in twos or

threes on Activity 2 then change round.
• **Activity 1. Estimating and measuring.** One set of scales, marbles (or other unit) per group. *Use Plasticine to make an apple which weighs about the same as 5 marbles. Use the scales to check. (Then make a carrot which weighs about the same as 3 marbles, etc.)*
• **Activity 2. Estimating and measuring: Copymaster 7.** 5 sets of scales and an apple, turnip, orange, carrot at each. Adjust the Copymaster to show the appropriate units of measure. *Make a 'good guess' of how many (units) each weighs, then weigh it on the scales. Record your 'good guess' and your measurement of the weighing.*

### Plenary

Discuss the activities. *Did your apple weigh about the same as 4 marbles?*
**Key idea.** We can use (units) to measure how much something weighs.

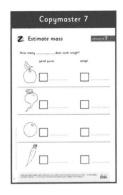

---

## DAY 4

*Suggest suitable non-standard units and measuring equipment to measure mass*

### Mental

Silly Sums: addition within 7
Guess the Number: for numbers between 10 and 20

### Main Session

• **Suitable units.** *Could we use marbles to weigh a feather? Why not? What might balance a feather?* (lentils, straw, etc.) *Would it be easy to balance a bag of potatoes with (units)? Why not? What could we use instead?* (pebbles, beanbags, etc.) Pass samples round for children to 'feel the heaviness'. Have a variety of balance scales (e.g. deep / shallow pans) and discuss their suitability for measuring different items.
• **Ordering units.** Small wooden or plastic cubes, beanbags, straws for each group. Ask children to compare the three types of (unit of) weight and put them in order from lightest to heaviest.

• **Choosing units: Recording Book page 11.** *Choose which unit – beanbags, cubes or straws – would be best to weigh the sweets, the spoon, the tin of dog food, the sock, the brick and the letter. Draw lines to match.* When task is completed ask children to explain their reasons for the choices they made. Weigh the items with different units.
• **Suitable units.** A set of scales at each group. Ask children to find things (from around the classroom or from items you offer) which can be measured using straws or cubes / marbles or beanbags, etc. They experiment with their suggestions.

### Plenary

Ask the groups to talk about their findings. *What did you measure with the cubes? Did they work well?*
**Key idea.** To measure heaviness I need to choose a suitable unit for weighing. ▐█

---

## DAY 5

*Use mental strategies to solve simple problems set in a measurement context, using counting, addition or halving, explaining methods and reasoning orally*

### Mental

In My Pocket: money problems within 7p
Ball Game Tens: counting on and back in tens

### Main Session

Divide class in two and change round as before.
• **Solving problems: Copymaster 8.** Work in pairs, of equal or mixed ability, to promote discussion and use the vocabulary related to mass. The Copymaster may be cut up or partly blanked out to limit the range. *Draw or*

*write the number to record your answers.*
• **Practical.** 5 or 6 'stations' with cards, scales and selection of units to use for measuring weight. Children work in twos or threes. Adjust numbers and units as appropriate and draw the bracketed items on the cards, e.g. card 1: How much heavier is the (orange) than the (apple)? 2: Find a (potato) = 3 marbles. 3: How much lighter is the (carrot) than the (turnip)? 4: How many (carrot) balance 3 (pebbles)? 5: How many (potato) balance 2 (orange)?

### Plenary

Discuss the activities. *How did you work out how many monkeys weigh the same as 6 buckets?*
**Key idea.** Balance scales can be used to help me solve problems about heaviness.

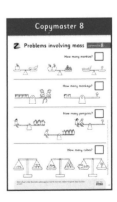

Sol Pr: **Reasoning about shapes**
M Sh Sp: **Shape and space**

Vocabulary: roll; stack; slide; face; corner; edge; fold; pattern; whole; equal parts; half
Resources: *Teacher* 3D shapes: cube, cuboid, sphere, cone, cylinder; 2D shapes: square, circle, triangle, rectangle; paper square; scissors; *Group* 3D shapes; construction kits; everyday materials; Plasticine; *Pair* a 1–6 dice; 18 counters; *Child* number cards; scissors; a paper square; circle and rectangle

## DAY 1

*Use everyday language to describe features of familiar 3D shapes; Begin to relate solid shapes to pictures of them; Describe movements*

### Mental

Hidden Shapes: 2D shapes
Card Game: facts to 8

### Main Session

• **Recognising shapes from pictures: Big Book pages 12&13.** Establish that the children are working with shapes, discuss what happens next, then concentrate on the 3D shapes. Ask children to name a shape in the picture, find and hold up the matching solid shape. Introduce *cylinder*.
• **Properties of 3D shapes.** Use solid shapes.

*Which shape has one curved face and one face that is a circle?* Repeat for cube, cylinder, cuboid and sphere. Then investigate for all (wooden or hard plastic) shapes: *Does it roll? Can it stack? Will it slide?*
• **Describing movements: Recording Book page 12.** Leave the shapes at each group to help the children work out the answers.

### Plenary

Put a shape in a large cloth bag and ask children to identify it by touch. *How do you know it is a cube?*
**Key idea.** We recognise a solid shape by the shape and number of its faces.

Big Book pages 12&13

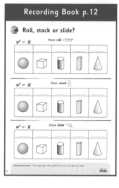
Recording Book p.12

## DAY 2

*Use everyday language to describe features of 2D shapes; Reason about shapes; Fold shapes in half, then make them into symmetrical patterns*

### Mental

Hidden Shapes: 3D shapes
Counting Stick: counting on and back in tens

### Main Session

• **Properties of 2D shapes; reasoning about shapes: Big Book pages 12&13.** Discuss the flat shapes used by Salma, Peter and Mo. *What has Salma made? Which shapes did she use?* etc. Discuss and establish the properties of circles, rectangles and squares.
• **Folding shapes in half.** Scissors, a paper circle, a square and a rectangle for each child. *Fold the circle in half. How many halves are there in one whole piece?*

*Are both halves exactly the same?* Issue rectangles. *Fold the rectangle in half.* Discuss the different ways the folding has been done. *Have they been folded in half? Do both parts match?* Issue squares. *Fold paper in half and draw a pattern that starts and ends on the fold. Cut along the line. Open the paper. Does your pattern balance on both sides of the fold?* Display the shapes made.
• **Recognising half: Recording Book page 13.** *Tick all the pictures where the line shows a half. Put a cross for those which do not.*

### Plenary

Discuss the display of shapes. *Does this pattern balance on both sides of the fold? The paper has been folded in two. What is each piece called?*
**Key idea.** When we fold a shape in half, both sides are the same size and they balance. █▌

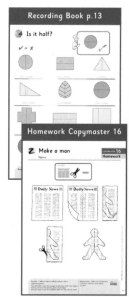
Recording Book p.13

Homework Copymaster 16
Make a man

## DAY 3

*Make and describe models, patterns and pictures using construction kits, everyday materials, Plasticine, etc.; Begin to relate solid shapes to pictures of them*

### Mental

Pandora's Bag: identify shape by touch
Number Cards: addition and subtraction facts to 8

### Main Session

• **Recognising shapes from pictures: Shared Activity Book page 8.** Each pair needs a 1–6 dice and 18 counters. Using the key, children cover the shapes. *Who is first to complete their building?* Alternative game if there are sufficient materials and space:

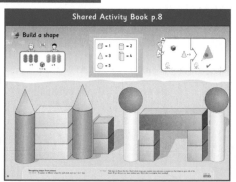
Shared Activity Book p.8
Build a shape

children throw the dice and win the actual solid shape to build the construction shown.
• **Making models.** Construction kits, everyday materials or Plasticine at each group. Either free choice or have some pictures of models to copy. Allow children time to build a model, then invite children to look at each other's.

## Plenary

*Which shapes have you used? Which ones are harder to use?* Ask a few children to describe how they made their models.
**Key idea.** To build a model we need to know which shapes stack.

---

## ASSESS and REVIEW

# Unit 7

| | |
|---|---|
| Number: | **Place value and ordering** |
| Calculations: | **Understanding addition and subtraction** |
| Sol Pr: | **Problems involving money** |
| M Sh Sp: | **Measures; Shape and space** |
| Vocabulary: | curved / flat face, corner, edge, round, straight; lighter, heavier, lightest, heaviest; count; total, add, together; more / less than; subtract |
| Resources: | *Group* 2D and 3D shapes in a bag; coins; 5 sets balance scales; 5 boxes marbles; 5 towers of Lego bricks; *Pair* 2 sets of number cards 0–12; 18 counters; number line; *Child* number cards 0–20 |

---

**DAY 1**

*Use everyday language to describe features of familiar 2D and 3D shapes; Measure a mass, understand the vocabulary related to mass; Count reliably; Understand the operation of addition and use the related vocabulary*

## Mental

Ball Game Twos: counting on and back in twos
Double Dare: doubling numbers to 6

## Main Session

• **2D and 3D shapes.** Bag containing a few mixed shapes at each group. In turn, child puts hands in and, without looking, describes the shape grasped. Others guess which shape it is. Stop after 5 minutes.
Have 5 'stations' ready, each with a set of simple balance scales, marbles for the unit of measure, and a tower of Lego bricks at each. The tower should weigh

an exact number of marbles and 12 marbles or less. Half the class line up to weigh the tower, then return to their seats to complete Recording Book page 14. The other half do Recording Book page 15. Change over after about 10 minutes.
• **Mass: Recording Book page 14.** Use flashcards to revise the reading of *lighter, heavier, lightest, heaviest. Use marbles to measure how much the tower weighs. Write your answer in the box. Then match the objects in the sections below to the correct labels.*
• **Counting and addition: Recording Book page 15.** *At the top of the page, count each group of objects, write the numbers in the boxes, then find the total. At the bottom of the page, add the numbers together and write the answer in the box.*

## Plenary

Discuss Recording Book page 14. *How much did the tower weigh? Explain how you measured it.*

Recording Book p.14

Review: weigh and compare

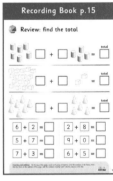
Recording Book p.15

Review: find the total

| | | | | | |
|---|---|---|---|---|---|
| 6 | + | 2 | = | | |
| 5 | + | 7 | = | | |
| 7 | + | 3 | = | | |

| | | | | | |
|---|---|---|---|---|---|
| 2 | + | 8 | = | | |
| 9 | + | 0 | = | | |
| 6 | + | 5 | = | | |

---

**DAY 2**

*Within the range 0–20, say the number that is 1 or 10 more or less than any given number; Solve simple problems set in money contexts; Understand the operation of subtraction and use the related vocabulary*

## Mental

Before and After Tens: ten more / less than any tens number to 100
Washing Line: ordering numbers to 20

## Main Session

• **Saying the number 1 or 10 more / less than.**
Number cards to 20. Children hold up their number cards to show 1 or 10 more / less than (number from 0–20).
• **Money problems; coins.** Children lay out a row of one each of 1p, 2p, 5p, 10p, 20p in front of them. Ask questions on equivalence; children hold up the

appropriate coin to answer, e.g. *Which coin is worth the same as five pennies? 2 × 5p? 10 × 2p? 20 × 1p?*, etc.
• **Subtraction: Shared Activity Book page 9.** Each pair needs 2 sets of number cards (0 to 12) mixed in a bag and 18 counters. *Take turns to remove 2 cards from the bag. Subtract the smaller number from the larger to find the answer. If the answer is on your board, cover it with a counter. Return the cards to the bag. Who is first to cover all their boxes?* Children may use a number line at your discretion.

## Plenary

Discuss the game. *How do we subtract two numbers? If both numbers are the same, what is the answer? How would you use a number line to subtract... from... ?*

Shared Activity Book p.9

A helping hand

Number: **Counting, properties of number and number sequences**
Sol Pr: **Reasoning about numbers**

Vocabulary: every other; odd; even; count on; count back; five more; two more
Resources: *Teacher* number cards 1–15; *Group* Multilink; coloured pencils; counters; paper for recording sums; *Pair* number cards 1–20; 2 dice (1–6) and 10 counters

**DAY 1**

**Begin to recognise odd or even numbers as 'every other number'**

## Mental

Make a Story: addition within 8
Clap and Count: to 40

## Main Session

• **Odd and even numbers: Big Book page 14.** *The children are getting ready for a go-kart race. How many children are there? How many have red hats? How many have blue hats?* On the board, list in order the numbers on the karts of those with red hats. Do the same with the blue hats. *What do you notice about the red hat numbers?* (odd) *the blue hat numbers?* (even) Look at **Big Book page 15.** *The children are lined up to start the race. Read the numbers* (1–20). *What do you notice about the numbers now?* (odd / even pattern) *When we count in ones, every other number is odd or even.* Read the numbers on page 14 again to reinforce the understanding. Then point to the numbers 1–20 again, but this time children say *odd, even, odd, even....*

• **Odd and even sticks.** Use Multilink to make sticks of numbers less than sixteen. *Can you split the stick into two equal parts? Are the sticks split evenly?* Look at the numbers from the red hats and make sticks of some of these numbers. *What do you notice when you split them in two?* Repeat for some blue hat numbers. Encourage the use of *odd* and *even* to describe the sets.

• **Is it odd or even?** Use a set of cards with numbers 1–15. Show cards in a random order. *Is this number odd / even? How do you know?*

• **Every other number.** Ask children to count round the class from 1 to 30, whispering / shouting out every other number, i.e. whisper *1*, shout *2*, whisper *3*, shout *4...* Ask those who whispered to stand. *Who is left sitting? What were their numbers?*

## Plenary

*How do you know when a number is even? How can we tell if it is odd? What was your number when we counted round the class? Is that an odd or an even number? What was the number before / after yours?*
**Key idea.** When we count in ones, every other number is odd or even.

Big Book pages 14 & 15

**DAY 2**

**Counting in twos from zero then one**

## Mental

In My Pocket: money problems within 8p
Think of a Number: adding or subtracting 1

## Main Session

• **Counting in twos: Big Book page 15.** *Look at the blue hats. Read their numbers. What kind of numbers are they?* (even) *Are they all even numbers? Now read the numbers on the red hats. What kind of numbers are they?* Discuss and establish that when we count in twos the numbers are either all odd or all even.

• **Counting in twos.** A set of number cards 0–20 per pair. Ask children to lay out the number cards in two rows across their tables. *Count in twos from zero, turning over the cards whose number you say. Which cards are now face up? face down?* Repeat the activity, starting at one.

• **Counting on and back in twos.** 20 Multilink per pair. *Push the Multilink together in sets of two.* Demonstrate counting in twos, sliding each set of 2 across as you count. *One of you count your Multilink in twos...2, 4....* Partner then counts back from 20, sliding the sets back across the table until zero is reached. Change places and repeat. *What is 2 more than... 2 less than?* etc.

• **Counting on and back in twos from one.** Repeat the activity, but start with one Multilink so the count goes 1, 3, 5, etc.

## Plenary

Discuss the counting from 0 activity. *How many were you counting on each time? What number did you start with? Were any of the numbers which came after 2 odd numbers? Why not?*
**Key idea.** When we count on in twos from an even number, the numbers are all even.

## DAY 3

**Count in steps of five to 20 or more, then back again**

### Mental

Thumbs Up, Thumbs Down: odd and even numbers
Silly Sums: addition and subtraction within 8

### Main Session

• **Counting in fives: Big Book page 15.** Draw the children's attention to the pattern of fives. *How many are in each row? What is the last number in each row? Count the cars in fives...5, 10, 15, 20.* Record this on the board. Ask a child to count in fives on the class number line and mark each 'station' with a blob of Blu-tack. *Everyone count in fives... and back again.*

• **Counting on and back in fives.** 30 Multilink per pair. *Push the Multilink into sets of 5. Count in fives to 30, and your partner counts back.* Repeat.

• **Counting on and back in fives.** Play 'Whisper, Shout' for fives. Count aloud round the class from 1 – every fifth person 'shouts' their number. Then count back in fives from 30.

• **Patterns of five: Recording book page 16.** *Fill in the missing numbers to complete the 5-pattern grid. Write the 5-pattern numbers from the shaded squares into the boxes underneath. Colour the 5-pattern on the number lines and then on the go-karts.*

### Plenary

*What pattern do you notice when you count in fives? What do the numbers end in?*

**Key idea.** When we count in fives the numbers end in five or zero.

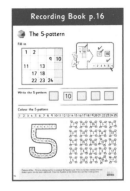
Recording Book p.16

---

## DAY 4

**Investigate a general statement about familiar numbers by finding examples that satisfy it; Explain methods and reasoning orally**

### Mental

Make a Story: subtraction within 8
Thumbs Up, Thumbs Down: odd and even numbers

### Main Session

• **Investigating a statement.** *If we add one to an odd number the answer is always even. How can we find out if this is true?* Discuss and establish the need to work out some addition sums to find out if the statement is correct. Allow time to experiment. Have counters and paper for recording available. Discuss the results. *Which numbers did you try? Were the answers always even? Why?*

• **Odd and even totals.** *Work together in pairs with two dice. Throw the dice and add the scores. Record your sums on a piece of paper.* When several sums have been recorded, discuss which totals are odd and which even. *How could you score seven? How could you score twelve?*

• **Odd and even numbers: Shared Activity Book page 10.** Each pair needs 10 counters and 2 dice (1–6). *The red team has the odd numbers and the blue team has the even numbers. Take turns to throw both dice. Add the scores together. If you make the number on one of your karts, put a counter on it. Who is first to cover all their karts?*

### Plenary

Discuss the game. *Were your numbers odd or even? How did you score 9? 6? Did anyone make an even number by adding two odd numbers?*

**Key idea.** Two odd numbers added together make an even number.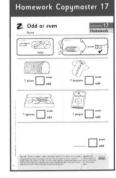

Shared Activity Book p.10

Homework Copymaster 17

---

## DAY 5

**Solve simple mathematical problems or puzzles, recognise and predict from simple patterns and relationships; Suggest extensions by asking What if...? or What could I try next?**

### Mental

Think of a Number: adding or subtracting 2
Silly Sums: addition and subtraction within 8

### Main Session

• **Recognising simple number patterns: Recording Book page 17.** *In each of the patterns there are two numbers missing. Look at the patterns and fill in the missing numbers.*

• **Adding the next number.** Use number cards 1–9. Select one card. *Which number follows this one?*

*Add the first number to the number which follows it. Is the answer odd or even?* Repeat the activity a few times. *Why is the answer always odd? What if you add the number two places along?*

• **Predicting.** Play in pairs with a set of number cards 1–9, shuffled. *Take 2 cards from the pile and look at the numbers. Before you add them, tell your partner whether the answer will be odd or even. Add them together and see if you were correct. Then your partner plays.*

### Plenary

Discuss the game. *Were you correct? If we add 2 even numbers together is the answer odd or even? If we add 2 odd numbers is the answer odd or even? If we add an odd and an even number?*

**Key idea.** Number patterns can often be used to help us work out the answers to problems.

Recording Book p.17

**Number:** Place value and ordering; Estimating
**Calculations:** Understanding addition and subtraction; Mental calculation strategies
**Vocabulary:** tens; ones; add; total; altogether; plus sign; equals sign; take away; difference; how many more to make
**Resources:** *Teacher* arrow cards; objects for estimating – a heap of beanbags, a bundle of pencils, a stack of books, a plastic bag of sweets, a wall of Lego bricks; 6 large card dominoes marked with spots in the patterns 5/0, 5/1, 5/2, 5/3, 5/4, 5/5; Blu-tack; *Group* sorting toys, counters, Multilink, marbles, beads, buttons, shells; set of dominoes; *Pair* bag with number cards 8–16 and 16 counters in 2 colours (8 of each)

---

**DAY 1**

**Partition larger two-digit numbers into a multiple of 10 and ones**

## Mental

Guess the Number: find the number between 2 others
Fast Facts to Five: addition within 5

## Main Session

• **Partitioning into tens and ones: Big Book pages 16&17.** Concentrate on the boat numbers. Ask a child to make each number using arrow cards, then ask questions such as *Which number is the lowest? highest? Count up from 11 to 29. In the number 15, what does the digit 1 stand for? What does the digit 5 stand for?*
• **Partitioning teens numbers.** Multilink. Each child makes a 10-rod with Multilink. *When I hold up an arrow card, you make the number using your 10-rod and some ones.* Make numbers between 11 and 19. Once children have laid out the Multilink each time, separate the arrow cards to make self-checking easy,

e.g. *17 is ten and seven ones.*
• **Partitioning larger numbers.** Multilink. *Work with a partner. Take turns to make the number shown on the arrow card and your partner checks.* Make numbers from 20 to 29, separating the arrow cards as before, after the numbers are made. *29 is twenty and nine ones. What number would be made with 3 tens? 4 tens? What number is fifty and 3 ones?* Demonstrate with Multilink then arrow cards and write the number on the board.

## Plenary

*What does the digit 2 stand for in 24? and the 4? Can anyone make their house number with arrow cards?*
**Key idea.** In a two-digit number, the first digit stands for the tens.

Big Book pages 16&17
Playing in the park (1)   Playing in the park (2)

---

**DAY 2**

**Understand and use the vocabulary of estimation; Estimate up to 30 objects**

## Mental

Arrow Card Game: for numbers 11 to 19
Five Fingers: subtraction within 5

## Main Session

• **Understanding estimation.** Multilink. Show a 10-rod from yesterday. *How many blocks are in this rod?* Break the rod into 10 pieces as children count and show them the pile of 10. Take a handful of about 15 blocks and place them beside the pile. *How many are in this pile? Make a 'good guess'.* Count to check and revise that they use something they already know (e.g. the pile of 10) to help make a 'good guess'. *What is a 'good guess'?* (one which is close to the actual amount) Repeat the activity with numbers in the range 11 to 19.
• **Estimates using known information: Big Book page 16.** *How many children are in the draughts group?* Display the page for a few seconds. *Now make a 'good guess' of how many children are in the dominoes group. Was that a 'good guess'? How did you do it?* Repeat for the other groups.

• **Estimation practice.** A selection of sorting toys, counters, Multilink, marbles, beads, buttons, shells. At each group have only one type of material available. Each child silently counts out a number of objects (between 15 and 25) and lays them in a heap on the table in front of him/her. Partners then make a 'good guess' of each other's numbers and count to check. Repeat a few times then change groups (or materials) so that children have practice with a different size.
• **Estimation puzzle: Recording Book page 18.** Set out 5 groups of objects: a heap of beanbags, a bundle of pencils, a stack of books, a plastic bag of sweets, a wall of Lego bricks. Children go round and record their 'good guess' on the page. Make sure they do not try to count the items illustrated on the page. Allow time to record then ask a few children to count the actual numbers, and all children record these. *Were you close to the actual amount? Did you make a 'good guess'? How did you make your 'good guess'?*

## Plenary

*When would we need to make a 'good guess'?* Discuss everyday occasions when we make a 'good guess', e.g. serving peas at lunch, giving handfuls of counters to children, cutting a piece of string to tie round a parcel.
**Key idea.** A 'good guess' is close to the actual amount.

Recording Book p.18
How many? Make a 'good guess'

## DAY 3

*Understand the operation of addition and use the related vocabulary; Begin to recognise that addition can be done in any order*

### Mental

Speedy Sixes and Sevens: addition and subtraction facts of 6 and 7
Counting Hat: counting on in twos

### Main Session

• **Understanding addition: Big Book page 17.**
Discuss the domino game and how it is played. Draw a domino on the board. With the children, count the spots on each side. *How many altogether?* Repeat. Write up the sums on the board; revise vocabulary *total, add,*

*altogether.*
• **Domino addition practice.** A set of dominoes per group. With a partner, children take a domino, and repeat the previous exercise; partner checks.
• **Adding in any order.** This time, after the first addition, turn the domino round; partner adds in the other order. *Are both answers the same?*
• **Writing addition sums: Recording Book page 19.** *Find the total number of spots on each domino. Write the sum beneath it, then work out the answer.*

### Plenary

Discuss the Recording Book page. *How did you find the total?* Discuss strategies used.
**Key idea.** Addition can be done in any order.

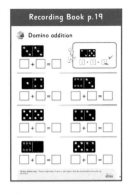

## DAY 4

*Understand the operation of subtraction and use the related vocabulary*

### Mental

Number Line Race: ten more / less than
Washing Line: ordering numbers 20 to 0

### Main Session

• **Understanding subtraction: Big Book pages 16&17.** Ask questions to revise subtraction vocabulary, e.g. *How many fewer children are playing draughts than dominoes?* Use the dominoes to identify numbers which are bigger, smaller, the same as; and to find the difference between the number of spots on each side.

• **Subtraction patterns of 10.** Use Multilink blocks: the children make 10-rods using two colours, to show all the number bonds to 10. Break the rods at the colour junction to show the different subtractions, e.g. 10 – 3 leaves 7, 10 – 7 leaves 3 etc. Use a wide vocabulary: *how many left, how many more to make,* etc. Invite the children to work in pairs, asking one another questions.
• **How many more to make: Recording Book page 20**. *Draw the objects needed to make the number. Then complete the sums.*

### Plenary

Discuss the Recording Book page. *When you had 6 spots, how many more were needed to make 8?*
**Key idea.** To find **how many more** are needed to make a number, we count on from the smaller number. ▐

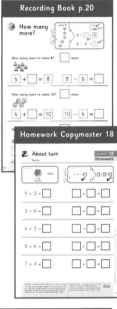

## DAY 5

*Begin to partition into 5 and a bit when adding 6, 7, 8 or 9, then recombine; Use patterns of similar calculations*

### Mental

Card Game: addition bonds of 9
Arrow Card Race: make numbers 10 to 20

### Main Session

• **Five and a bit.** Use dominoes marked 5 + 3 and 5 + 1. *How many spots on this domino altogether? and on this one? 8 add 6, how many spots altogether? How did you work it out?* Demonstrate how the answer could be found by using facts already known: adding 5 + 5, then 3 + 1, then adding 10 and 4.
• **Quick addition.** A set of 6 large (card) dominoes with 5 spots on one side and 0 to 5 spots on the other. Blu-tack two of them to the board and ask children to find the total number of spots as quickly as possible. Discuss how the answer was found. Encourage the use of 5 and a bit partitioning or other strategies which children may prefer to use.

• **Patterns of similar calculations.** Blu-tack the large dominoes to the board in a column, in order from 5/0 to 5/5. Opposite each write the equals sign. *What is the total number of spots on each domino?* As you write in the answers, draw children's attention to the number pattern increasing by one each time, which makes it easy to predict the next answer. *Subtract the spots on the right from 5. Answer quickly!*

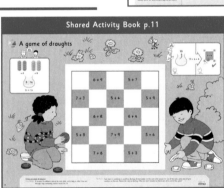

• **Using mental strategies: Shared Activity Book page 11.** Each pair needs number cards 8–16 and 16 counters in 2 colours. Players withdraw cards and cover a sum with a counter if it matches. Encourage partner to check by doing the sum a different way.

### Plenary

Discuss the game and how the answers were calculated.
**Key idea.** There is a often a quick way to work out the answer to a sum.

**Sol Pr:** Problems involving 'real life' and money; Making decisions

Vocabulary: coins; price; costs more / less than; the same as; change; exchange; how much; how much more; doubling; halving

Resources *Group* coins; *Pair* 2 × 1p, 2 × 2p, 2 × 5p, 2 × 10p coins and a cloth bag; number cards 11–19 and coins; a 1–6 dice and coins; coins, a real coin, 2 counters and a 1–6 dice; *Child* number lines; number cards

### Understand the vocabulary related to money; Recognise coins of different values

## Mental

I Know My Coins: making exact amount
Guess the Number: find the number between 2 others

## Main Session

• **Money vocabulary: Big Book pages 18&19.** Discuss the car boot sale and then concentrate on page 18. Use the vocabulary *costs more / less, price, how much, e.g. What is the price of a large cake?*(£2) *How much does a scarf cost?*(50p) *Which costs more, the jug or the vase?*

• **Coin recognition.** Coins. Children hold up the appropriate coin in response to questions such as *A picture costs £1. Show me a £1 coin.* Repeat for large cake (£2), scarf (50p), vase (20p), jug (10p), buttons (5p), magazines (2p) and buttons (1p).

• **Equivalence.** Coins. *We do not always pay with one coin. How else could we pay for a comic which costs*

*2p?* Ensure that children understand the meaning of the term *exchange. How many pennies make 5p? How many pennies can we exchange for a 10p coin? Which 2 coins together make 10p? 20p?* Ask children to lay out the coins on their tables each time as this reinforces the equivalent value.

• **Equivalence: Recording Book page 21.** *Draw a line to join each group of coins to the single coin which is worth the same amount.*

## Plenary

Discuss the Recording Book page. *Which coin is worth the same as 5 pennies? is worth the same as 2 fivepences? two pennies? Is there another way to make 2p? Why not?*

**Key idea.** We can exchange a larger coin for a group of coins of smaller value.

Big Book pages 18&19

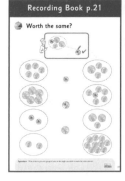
Recording Book p.21

### Find totals and change from up to 20p

## Mental

In My Pocket: money problems within 9p
Pandora's Bag: identify shape by touch

## Main Session

• **Giving change: Big Book page 18.** *Zoe has 20p to spend. How much change would she get if she bought a bag of chocolate fudge? How can we work it out?* Ask children to demonstrate, using a number line and counting on in ones, or start at 18p and count out the pennies for the change.

• **Practising giving change.** Coins, number lines, number cards. Ask questions about the articles for sale. Children lay out the change from 20p and hold up a number card to show the answer. They can also use a

number line to help them, e.g. *Anna bought a ribbon which cost 16p. Lay out her change from 20p. How much change did she get?* Discuss answers. *Did anyone lay out different coins? Is that also correct?*

• **Finding totals.** 2 × 1p, 2 × 2p, 2 × 5p, 2 × 10p coins and a cloth bag per pair. *Work with a partner. In turn take 2 coins from the bag and find their total value. Your partner checks and the coins are returned to the bag.* Limit the coins used to provide differentiation. Extend to taking 3 coins from the bag.

• **Finding totals: Recording Book page 22.** Number lines and / or coins should be available. *Add the coins in each purse and write the total amount in the box.*

## Plenary

Discuss the Recording Book page. *How much altogether is 10p, 1p and 5p? How did you work it out?*

**Key idea.** You can give change by counting on in ones.

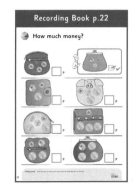
Recording Book p.22

## DAY 3

### Work out how to pay an exact sum

## Mental

In My Pocket: money problems within 9p
Before and After: one before / after any number to 30

## Main Session

• **Making an exact amount: Big Book page 18.** *How much is the fudge? Which coins would you use to make that amount exactly?* Ask a few children to select coins and make 18p. Discuss the results. *Does this make 18p? Mary has made it a different way, is she still correct? Why?* Repeat for car at 16p and ribbon at 15p.
• **Practice.** Coins, one set of number cards 12–19 per pair. *Work with a partner. Take 4 cards each and lay them on your table. Beside each card, lay out the coins to make exactly that amount.* Partner counts to check.
• **Making amounts: Shared Activity Book page 12.**

Each pair needs coins and a 1–6 dice. Before playing demonstrate how to select coins to make the number shown, e.g. if a 5 is thrown they may choose a 5p or $5 \times 1p$ or $2 \times 2p + 1p$, etc. *Take turns to throw the dice. Look at the number and take a coin or coins to make that number. Put coins on the hands on your side to make the amount shown. Who is first to make both amounts?*

## Plenary

Discuss the game. *How did you make 12p? Is there another way? How many coins did you use to make 15p? Did anyone use more / fewer coins? What did you find difficult when playing this game?*
**Key idea.** To make an exact amount we must use coins which add up to the total.

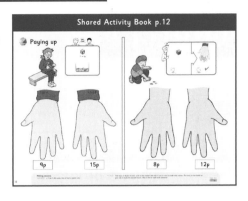

Shared Activity Book p.12

---

## DAY 4

### Choose and use appropriate number operations and mental strategies to solve problems; Explain methods and reasoning orally

## Mental

I Know My Coins: making exact amount
Number Cards: addition and subtraction facts to 9

## Main Session

• **Number operations.** Children use number cards to show their responses. After each simple problem, discuss which kind of sum they had to do to work out the answer, and help them to realise that the clues are in the words. **1.** *I have 6p and 3p. How much altogether?* **2.** *Anna has 6 beads. How many more does she need to make 10?* **3.** *Rob has 20p. Zoe has 2p less. How much does she have?* **4.** *Which 2 coins together make 7p?*

• **Deciding and choosing.** Tell the children you have a secret amount of money. They ask you how much more you need to make 10p. *What is my secret amount?* Discuss the first answer and ask children to explain how they worked it out. *How did you decide which kind of sum to do? How did you choose to do it?* (mentally, using coins, a number line)
• **Money problems: Recording Book page 23.** *Zoe has 20p altogether. Count how much is in the open hand and then work out how much is hidden in the other hand. Write the answer in the box.*

## Plenary

Discuss the Recording Book page. *What was your answer to the first puzzle? Explain how you worked it out. Did you use anything to help you? Why (not)? Did anyone do it another way?*
**Key idea.** You know which kind of sum to do by thinking about the words used in the problem. ▊

Recording Book p.23

Homework Copymaster 19

---

## DAY 5

### Use mental strategies to solve simple money problems using doubling or halving

## Mental

Pandora's Bag: identify shapes by touch
Make a Story: addition or subtraction within 9

## Main Session

• **Halving: Big Book page 19.** Coins. *At the end of the sale, Max's mum sold off everything at half price. What does half price mean? What is half of 2p? Can you work out what other items would cost?* Discuss and encourage children to think of the coins which would make the whole amount (a 2p or $2 \times 1p$). Ask a child to demonstrate. Repeat for 10p, then 20p, then 16p. If appropriate, discuss what half of £1 would be.
• **Doubling coins.** Coins. Show a 1p coin. *How much is this? If I doubled this coin* (demonstrate) *how much*

*would I have?* Repeat for 2p, 5p and 10p.
• **Double your money: Shared Activity Book page 13.** Each pair needs coins, 2 counters and a 1–6 dice. *Take turns to throw the dice to move. When you land on a yellow square, flip the coin. If it lands heads up, take double the amount shown in the box. If it lands tails up, take half the amount shown. Who has the most money at the end of the game?*

## Plenary

Discuss the game. *Who won? Why was that? What is half of 6p? double 4p? How much did you win altogether? Who had more? less?*
**Key idea.** To double something we take two lots.

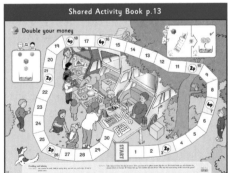

Shared Activity Book p.13

**M Sh Sp:** Measures – Time

Vocabulary: o'clock; hour; hands; earlier; later; morning; afternoon; evening; night; before; after; midday; midnight; watch; Monday – Sunday; today; yesterday; tomorrow

Resources: *Teacher* 6 small clock faces; Blu-tack; geared clock; large flashcards of days of the week; simple timer which can be set for one minute; real clock; *Group* (see Day 5) choice of Lego, Multilink, beads and string, squared paper, Plasticine, jigsaws, bricks; *Pair* coin; 2 counters; 2 clock faces; *Child* clock faces; number lines

### Understand and use the vocabulary related to time; Read the time to the hour on analogue clocks

## Mental

Days of the Week 1: sequence
Fast Facts to Five: addition and subtraction to 5

## Main Session

• **Reading the time: Big Book pages 20&21.** 6 small clock faces and a geared clock. Discuss Jim's day and decide what he is doing in each picture (arriving at school / writing a story / playing in the yard at break / eating lunch / painting a picture / riding his bike). Revise telling the time to the hour using the geared clock. Refer to the labels in the Big Book pages, ask children to read the times, set the small clocks to these times and Blu-tack them to the appropriate picture.
• **Using time vocabulary.** Geared clock. Ask children to think of something they do at 8 o'clock in the morning. Ask a child to set the hands of the clock to

8 o'clock and tell what they did at that time. Repeat for other times or allow children to choose their own times to talk about and show. Encourage the use of time vocabulary such as *Who gets up earlier / later? Is that in the morning, afternoon or evening? When is the afternoon? What do you do before eating supper? after school? at midnight?*
• **Clock faces: Recording Book page 24.** *The clock faces have numbers missing. Write the missing numbers in the gaps, then write the time shown on each clock.*

## Plenary

Discuss the Recording Book page. *Which number is always at the top? at the bottom? Read the times on the clocks.*
**Key idea.** When the big hand points to 12 it is an o'clock time.

Big Book pages 20&21

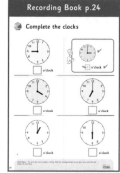

Recording Book p.24

### Read the time to the hour; Know and use units of time and the relationships between them

## Mental

Speedy Sixes and Sevens: addition and subtraction of 6 and 7
Ball Game Twos: counting on and back in twos

## Main Session

• **Telling the time.** A large clock face for you and a small clock face for each child. Set the hands, but hide your clock as you give instructions, e.g. *My big hand points to 12 and my little hand points to 3. What time is it?* Show your clock face and children check the time they have made on their clocks. Invite a child to be the 'teacher' and set the large clock, etc.

• **Recording the time: Recording Book page 25.** *The big hand is drawn for you on the first 6 clocks. Draw in the little hand to make the time shown. On the last 2 clocks draw both hands to make the time shown.*
• **Relationships.** Geared clock. Set the time at 1 o'clock. *Watch what happens as the clock moves on to 2 o'clock. How long is it from 1 o'clock until 2 o'clock? When is midday? midnight? How many hours from 1 o'clock until 12 o'clock midday? What time is it one hour after midday?* etc. Explain that there are 12 hours in the first half of the day and 12 hours in the second half. *How many hours altogether in one day?*

## Plenary

*How did you show 9 o'clock in your Recording Book? How many hours are in one day?*
**Key idea.** There are 24 hours in one day.

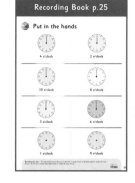

Recording Book p.25

### Know the days of the week; Know and use units of time and the relationships between them

## Mental

Days of the Week 2: day before / after
Card Game: addition bonds of 10

## Main Session

• **Days of the week.** Large flashcards with names of the days. Revise orally the sequence of the days of the week then introduce the reading of the days. Blu-tack them to the board and ask questions. Child comes out to point to the name to show the answer, e.g. *Which day is it today? Which day comes before Tuesday?*

- **Relationship of days / week.** Flashcards. Jumble up the flashcards and ask the class to help you stick them up in order starting with Monday. Read the names together. *What do 7 days make altogether? If we start on Monday and go through all the days in the week* (read them together) *what comes next? How many days are in one week? hours are in one day?*
- **Knowing the days of the week: Recording Book page 26.** *Put a tick beside the correct day and a cross*

*beside the wrong one. Match the last picture to the name to show what day it is today.*

## Plenary

Discuss the Recording Book page. *Which day do we go to school – on Saturday or Monday? How many days are in a week? On how many days do we come to school?*
**Key idea.** There are 7 days in a week.

Recording Book p.26

**DAY 4**

*Solve problems set in a time content, explaining methods and reasoning orally*

## Mental

Days of the Week 1: sequence
Number Cards: addition and subtraction facts to 10

## Main Session

- **Calculating time: Big Book pages 20&21.** Geared clock, small clocks for children. *What time did Jim arrive at school? What time is it when he is writing his story? How long is it from 9 o'clock until 10 o'clock? How did you work it out? Did anyone do it another way?* Explain how to work it out by counting on. Repeat for several examples. *When was Jim riding his bike?* Set the geared clock to 5 o'clock. *What time will it be in one hour?* Move the hands to demonstrate and verify the answer. Reset to 5 o'clock and repeat for *What time was it an hour ago?* Show a variety of times and ask children to respond to your questions by setting the hands on their clocks.

- **How long between: Recording Book page 27.** Number lines. *The first clock shows when the journey started. The second shows when the journey finished. Find how many hours each journey took.*
- **Timing a journey: Shared Activity Book page 14.** Each pair needs 2 small clock faces, a coin and 2 counters. *Set your clock to 1 o'clock. Flip the coin to move. If it shows 'heads' move your counter on 2. If it is 'tails' move your counter on 1. If you land on a picture, move your clock hands forward the number of hours shown. Keep going until you both reach the seaside. What time is shown on your clock?*

## Plenary

Discuss the game. *What time was it when you left? and when you arrived? How long between both times? How long did your journey take?*
**Key idea.** To find how long it is between two times, we count on from the first time.

Recording Book p.27

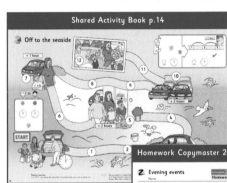
Shared Activity Book p.14

Homework Copymaster 20

**DAY 5**

*Solve problems set in a time content, explaining methods and reasoning orally*

## Mental

Days of the Week 2: day before / after
Ball Game Doubles: doubling numbers to 8

## Main Session

- **Using a timer.** Simple timer, working clock, number cards 0–20, child's jacket. To give children a sense of the length of a minute, ask them to watch the clock for a minute (to see the hand move), then set the timer for a minute and wait until it buzzes. *Which of these activities do you think would take one minute? Take 40 giant steps, lay out number cards from 0 to 20, put on a jacket and fasten it?* Volunteers experiment with each activity. Time them and discuss the results.
- **Estimating and checking.** Simple timer. Select resources to match chosen activities: Lego, squared paper, beads and string, Plasticine, jigsaws, bricks.

It may be easier to involve all the children by doing this part of the session in the gym hall and adjusting the activities to suit. Alternative suggestions are given here. *How many giant steps can you take in one minute? How many bunny hops could you do in one minute? Make a 'good guess'.* Experiment and check the answer. *Was it a 'good guess'? Why? Why not?* Ask children to suggest activities which could be done in a minute. Other suggestions to choose from: *How many Lego bricks can you join in one minute? How many boxes can be coloured in? beads can be threaded? Plasticine mice made?*
- **Using a timer.** Use the timer to time an activity: build a jigsaw, build a castle, write all the numbers from 0 to 20.

## Plenary

Ask the children to explain their activities, and how close they could make their estimate. Try out a few of the children's 'one minute' suggestions.
**Key idea.** A timer is used to measure time exactly.

**Sol Pr:** Organising and using data

**Vocabulary:** list; table; display; information; favourite; sort; most; least popular

**Resources:** *Teacher* 5 packets of crisps in different flavours with different coloured bags; sheets of paper; Blu-tack; 4 large sheets of card (if needed); *Group* bricks or Multilink; glue; one type per group of beads, counters, bricks, sorting toys; *Pair* a 1–6 dice; 2 counters and access to the group's objects; *Child* scissors

**DAY 1**

Solve a given problem by sorting and organising information, using objects, in a list or simple table

## Mental

Ball Game Doubles: doubling numbers to 9
Tricky Sixes: addition and subtraction to 6

## Main Session

• **Making lists and tables: Big Book page 22.** Discuss the picture of the children arriving at school. *How many people are getting off the bus? How many are walking? Which other ways did they travel to school?* List all the different ways on the board. *This is a list of how the children came to school.* Draw lines to make the list into a table with 'travel' and 'number' as the headings. Ask children to count the numbers and complete the table. Children then use the table to answer questions such as *How did most children travel to school? How many more walked than came by car? How many children are in the picture? How many have we included altogether in our table?*

• **Using objects to display.** Bricks. *How could we show the same information using objects?* Discuss the suggestions and then make towers of bricks using a different colour for each category to display the information. *How many children came by car? by bike? Does the tower display show exactly the same information as before?*

• **Using objects to solve a problem.** 5 packets of crisps in different flavours and different coloured bags. *Which flavour of crisps do you like best? How can we find out how many people like cheese flavour best? How could we find out using objects?* Discuss then ask children to place colour-coded bricks in a tower beside their favourite flavours. *Have we counted everybody? How do you know?*

• **Making a table.** *How could we show this information in a table?* Discuss, leading the children to suggest that they need to count the bricks. *What needs to go at the top of a table?* **Recording Book page 28.** *Look at your class display showing which flavour people like. Draw a crisp packet in each colour to show the flavours. Write in the number of bricks to complete the table.*

## Plenary

Discuss the Recording Book page. *How many liked x flavour best? Which did most people like best? How did you make the table?*

**Key idea.** A table displays information clearly.

Big Book p.22 — Travelling to school

Recording Book p.28 — Fill in the table

| flavour | number |
|---|---|
|  |  |
|  |  |
|  |  |
|  |  |

**DAY 2**

Solve a given problem by sorting and organising information in a simple table and by using pictures

## Mental

Children's Challenge: facts to 10
Before and After Tens: to 100

## Main Session

• **Showing information in a table: Big Book page 23.** Discuss the picture of the school pet show. *Which kind of pet is the most popular?* Ask children to think about how the answer to this can be shown. *Which different kinds of pets are there?* List on the board. *How can this list be made into a table?* Ask a child to draw the lines to make the list into a table and others enter the information as it is given: *How many budgies are there? dogs?* etc. Ask questions about the completed table. *Which kind of pet is the least common?*

• **Using pictures: Copymaster 9** cut into 3 strips. Scissors and glue. *Here are some of the pets from the pet show. Make a display so we can see which of these pets are the favourites.* Discuss the steps needed: collect, sort and arrange / make a display. **Recording Book page 29.** *Cut round each box to separate the pictures of the pets. Sort them, then glue them on this page of your Recording Book to make a display.*

## Plenary

Discuss the activity. *How many dogs are in your display? Are there more dogs than cats? Which is the most popular pet? How did you use pictures to solve the problem?* (revise the steps)

**Key idea.** We collect, sort and display the information, then we use it to solve the problem.

Big Book p.23 — School pet show — Pet Show

Copymaster 9 — Pet show data pictures

Recording Book p.29 — Animals at the pet show

Solve a given problem by sorting and organising information in simple ways

## Mental

Names and Numbers: numerals and names to 20
Pandora's Bag: identify shapes by touch

## Main Session

• **Collecting: Shared Activity Book page 15.** Divide the class into 4 groups. Each group is given a different type of object to collect in a variety of colours, e.g. beads, counters, bricks or sorting toys. Each pair needs a 1–6 dice and 2 counters, and access to group box of objects. *Take turns to throw the dice and move. If the number on the dice answers the question on the square you land on, take the number of objects shown. If not, then do not take any objects. Who has most objects at the end of the game?* Stop the game when suitable, to limit the number of objects required. Each child keeps beside them the objects won in the game.

• **Solving a problem.** Have sheets of paper, Blu-tack

and 4 large sheets of card available if the children request them. Explain that the group's task is to show the information so that others can answer these questions: *Who won most objects in your group? Who won least? How many objects were won altogether?* Review the ways they know of displaying information: in a list, in a table, using objects, using pictures. *Discuss how you are going to do it, then work together to display the information.*

Shared Activity Book p.15

## Plenary

Arrange the completed displays for all to see and ask children from a different group to answer the key questions: *Who won most objects? Who won least? How many objects were won altogether?* Discuss the displays and ask children to explain why they chose that way to show the information.

**Key idea.** There are different ways to display the same information.

Homework Copymaster 21

Find the favourite

---

Revision
The teacher decides how to use these two days. Time can be spent on giving some children extra help where they are insecure, teaching new ideas to children who have been absent, or providing additional practice to revise work already covered, before tackling the assessment and review unit.

No daily programme is given. The teacher may select from the list of key Shared Activity Games to revisit an activity, and a Copymaster which provides additional practice in addition and subtraction.

## Mental

Children's Challenge: facts to 10
Ball Game Tens: to 100
Arrow Card Race: to 30
Number Cards: addition and subtraction facts to 10

## Shared Activity Games

**Page 3 – Toys number track.** Addition and subtraction. 2 counters, 1 dice and a strip of number facts from Copymaster 2.

**Page 5 – Make a picture.** Facts of 10. Copymasters 4&5.

**Page 6 – Funny lunch!** Decide whether to add or subtract. 2 dice (1–6) and 12 counters in 2 colours.

**Page 9 – A helping hand.** Subtraction within 12. 2 sets of number cards (0 to 12) mixed in a bag, 18 counters and a number line.

**Page 11 – A game of draughts.** Mental calculations. Number cards 8–16 and 16 counters in 2 colours.

**Page 12 – Paying up.** Making amounts of money. Coins and a 1–6 dice.

**Page 14 – Off to the seaside.** Time. 2 small clock faces, a coin and 2 counters.

**Copymaster 10.**
The top half provides practice in addition within 12.
The bottom half provides practice in subtraction within 12.

Copymaster 10

Add/subtract within 12

# Unit 13

**Number:** Counting, properties of number and number sequences; Place value and ordering
**Calculations:** Understanding addition and subtraction; Rapid recall
**Sol Pr:** Making decisions; Problems involving money or time
**M Sh Sp:** Measures – Time

**Vocabulary:** clock, hands, an hour ago; tens, units; odd; total, change; altogether, more than, less than

**Resources:** *Teacher* geared clock; *Pair* a 1–6 dice and 2 counters; *Child* clock faces; number cards 0–9; number lines; 9 pennies

---

## DAY 1

Read the time to the hour and *solve problems* involving time; Begin to partition larger two-digit numbers into tens and units; *Understand the operation of addition and subtraction*

### Mental

Names and Numbers: numerals and names to 20
Think of a Number: one / ten before / after a number

### Main Session

• **Reading the time; time problems.** Geared clock and small clock faces. Hide your clock from the class and set the hands. *Set your clock hands to 5 o'clock.* Turn your clock round and children check the time on each other's clocks. Change the questions to *Look at the time on my clock. What time was it an hour ago? What time will it be 3 hours from now?*

• **Partitioning into tens and units.** Number cards 0–9. Children hold up the appropriate number card in response to questions such as *How many tens are in 24? How many units? Show me how many tens and how many units make the number 35.*

• **Addition and subtraction: Recording Book page 30.** *Work out the answer to each sum then draw a circle round the 'odd' one out. (5 + 6 = 11: the answer is the only odd number)*

### Plenary

Discuss the Recording Book page. *Which was the odd one out? Why? Is it the only answer that is an odd number? What is an even number?*

Recording Book p.30

---

## DAY 2

Count on or back in steps of five; doubling; Find totals and change from 20p; Choose and use appropriate number operations and mental strategies to *solve problems* in 'real life'

### Mental

Whisper, shout: play in 2s and 5s
Number Cards: addition and subtraction facts to 10

### Main Session

• **Solving a problem: Big Book page 24.** Explain how the darts game is played: each child throws three Velcro darts and adds up the score for those that stick on the board. *How did Rob score 8? Is there another way to get that score? Someone didn't add up correctly. Can you work out who it was?*

• **Doubling: Shared Activity Book page 16.** Each pair needs a 1–6 dice and 2 counters. *Take turns to throw the dice to move. If you land on a red space, double your score and move on. If you land on a 'penalty' space, move back as indicated. First to reach the finish is the winner.*

• **Change from 20p: Recording Book page 31.** Number lines. *Find the total cost of each child's sweets, then work out the change from 20p.*

• **Solving a problem.** 9 pennies each. *Max, Eva and Rob have 9 pennies altogether. Eva has 2 pennies more than Max, who has 2 pennies more than Rob. Lay out the pennies to show how much each has.* Repeat the question as the children are working.

### Plenary

Discuss the problem. *How many pennies did each have? How did you work it out? Did anyone do it another way? How did the words help you?*

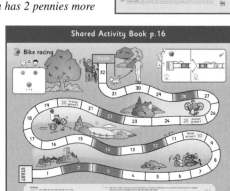
Big Book p.24

Shared Activity Book p.16
Bike racing

Recording Book p.31

# Mental Activities

| Activity name | What you need | What you do |
|---|---|---|
| Arrow Card Game | large arrow cards; individual number cards | Hold up a 'teens' number made with 2 arrow cards and asks children to hold up the 2 cards which make the number, i.e. *a ten and a ...* |
| Arrow Card Race | flashcards displaying written number names 10–20; 2 sets large arrow cards | Choose two teams. Hold up flashcard displaying a number name, a player from each team is at the set of arrow cards and makes the number. First to hold it up, correctly made, scores a point for the team. |
| Ball Game Doubles | soft foam ball | Throw / roll a soft foam ball to a child saying a number as you throw. Child catches ball and doubles the number before throwing it back to you. |
| Ball Game Tens | soft foam ball | Throw / roll a soft foam ball to a child at random, saying *zero*. Child catches ball and throws it back, saying *ten* and so on. When 50 is reached, count backwards. |
| Ball Game Twos | soft foam ball | A soft foam ball is passed around the class. Children count in twos starting with zero. When 20 is reached count back to zero. |
| Before and After | number flashcards; individual number cards | Number cards. *Lay out your cards in order, numbered side up. When I hold up a number you hold up the number which is **one after.*** Repeat several times. Use children to call numbers. Change procedure to *hold up the number which is **one before.*** Vary by using the number names. |
| Before and After Tens | individual number cards | Children hold up cards to show the number ten before / after the one called. |
| Bigger and Smaller | number flashcards | Say a number aloud then hold up a flashcard showing another number. Class show whether the number shown is bigger / smaller than the first number by holding both hands high (it's bigger than) or holding both hands low (it's smaller than). |
| Card Game | number flashcards; individual number cards | Choose a set of cards, e.g. 0–5. *Our sums must add to 5.* Hold up 3. *Hold up the number we need to add to this number to make 5.* Ask a child to write the sum on the board. The whole class then reads it aloud together. Work through the bonds for 5. Vary by using children to choose and hold up the flashcard number. |
| Children's Challenge | | Split the class into 2 teams of mixed ability. A child from team 1 calls out the name of a child in team 2 and asks a question. (Set the type of sum to be asked throughout the game, e.g. adding on 1.) Child in team 2 answers, scores a point if correct and then asks a question of a child in team 1. Encourage random selection of players to be asked the questions to keep everyone on their toes. |
| Clap and Count | | Count to a clapping rhythm, until a target number is reached. |
| Counting Hat | hat with +2 stuck on the front | Place the hat on a child's head as you say *zero*. Child counts on 2, saying the number aloud and quickly passes hat to next child. When 20 is reached, start again. Later vary the game by starting the counting at *one*. |
| Counting Stick | metre rule marked with 10 cm strips in alternate colours | Use for counting in 1s, 10s, etc. |
| Days of the Week 1 | | Recite the days of the week round the class, each child saying the next day of the week. Watch out for children who are slow / cannot respond and check to see how much they can remember. |
| Days of the Week 2 | day flashcards | Hold up a flashcard of a day and ask children to name the day before / after. |
| Double Dare | number cards | Someone holds a set of cards from 0 to 5 (or more if appropriate). The cards are fanned out, faces hidden. A child pulls out a card at random and then has to double the number shown on the card. Display to class to verify. |

| Activity name | What you need | What you do |
|---|---|---|
| Fast Facts to Five | | Speed quiz practising addition facts within 5. Perhaps this could be a team / group challenge to keep interest going. |
| Five Fingers | | Hold up hand showing five fingers then hold hand up again showing a number from 0 to 5 and say *take away / subtract / minus / find the difference between / how many are left* to practise the vocabulary recently learned. Children observe the number of fingers shown and calculate the answer. |
| Guess the Number | number flashcards | Hide a flashcard behind your back and ask *This is a number between 5 and 7 what is it?* When children are familiar with the game allow them to select a card and ask the questions. |
| Hidden Shapes | 2D shapes | Use shapes hidden behind a screen, slowly revealing them for the children to name. |
| I Know My Coins | 4 boxes of coins | Divide class into 4 teams. Place the boxes of coins on the floor / chair. One from each team stands beside each box. Call out a coin, child makes the coin's value using other coins to make the equivalent amount, e.g. *5p* can be shown as $5 \times 1p$ or $2 \times 2p + 1p$. First with any correct solution wins a point. |
| In My Pocket | | *In my pocket I have (number) pennies. I go to the shop and spend 3p. How much is left?* |
| Make a Story | number cards | Child pulls out 2 cards from pile and has to make up a sum and set it in a context. Class volunteer the answer and the child who answers correctly pulls out the next 2 cards. |
| Names and Numbers | number flashcards; individual number cards | *Lay out your cards in order, number side up. Start with zero.* Hold up a flashcard showing a number name and children hold up the corresponding numeral. |
| Number Cards | number cards 1–20 | Ask questions so that the answers can be held up by the children, such as: *show me 2 more than 7, show me 1 less than 15* and also use for number bond practice. |
| Number Line Race | number line marked only in tens from 0 to 100 | Divide class into 4 teams and a player from each comes forward and sits down. Ask a question (*ten more / less than, which tens number is between... and...*). First to stand up is allowed to go to the number line to point to the answer and if correct, scores a point for the team. |
| Pandora's Bag | 3D shapes; feely bag | Place a shape in the bag. Child puts hands in and identifies the shape by touch. |
| Silly Sums | individual number cards | The intention here is to speed up computation in a fun way and to use different language involving addition and / or subtraction within a given number. Children use their cards to hold up their answer, thus enabling you to involve and monitor everyone at the same time. When making up a Silly Sum always use the name of someone in the class or school, e.g. *John has 3 elephants in one pocket and 1 in another. How many elephants does he have altogether?* |
| Speedy Sixes and Sevens | individual number cards | Call out addition or subtraction facts for 6 or 7. Class hold up the correct card to show the answer. Keep the pace fast to maintain interest. |
| Think of a Number | individual number cards | *I think of a number then add (or take away) 1. The answer is (number). What was my number?* Later extend the range of numbers. Children hold up card to show the answer. |
| Thumbs Up, Thumbs Down | | Call out a number. Children hold thumbs up if it is an even number, thumbs down if it is an odd number. |
| Tricky Sixes | individual number cards | Call out number facts to 6. If the answer is 0 to 5 children hold up the appropriate card. If the answer is 6, they do not hold up the card but call out *six!* |
| Washing Line | washing line; cards / pegs 0–20 | Place 0 and the chosen end number on a washing line, children then peg up individual digit cards in order on the line. |
| Whisper, shout 2s and 5s | | Count aloud round the class from 1 to 30. Every second/fifth child shouts their number; the rest whisper theirs. Count back. |

# Bingo cards

| 10 | 7 | 20 |
|----|----|----|
| 19 | 2 | 17 |

| 13 | 6 | 5 |
|----|----|----|
| 8 | 11 | 4 |

| 20 | 5 | 3 |
|----|----|----|
| 12 | 16 | 14 |

| 9 | 1 | 13 |
|----|----|----|
| 7 | 12 | 15 |

| 19 | 15 | 17 |
|----|----|----|
| 3 | 10 | 6 |

| 2 | 16 | 13 |
|----|----|----|
| 7 | 19 | 8 |

| 18 | 4 | 15 |
|----|----|----|
| 6 | 20 | 9 |

| 11 | 9 | 17 |
|----|----|----|
| 1 | 12 | 18 |

Photocopy, cut up and issue as bingo cards. Call *one more / less than...* or *one before / after...*
Child crosses out the answer. Photocopied 4 times for a class of 32, there will be 4 winners.

**Y 1 T 2**
**Unit 2**

# Sum strips

| | | | | | |
|---|---|---|---|---|---|
| 1 + 1 = 2 | 4 + 1 = 5 | 4 − 2 = 2 | 4 + 2 = 6 | 5 − 0 = 5 | |
| 2 − 1 = 1 | 6 − 1 = 7 | 3 + 2 = 5 | 3 − 1 = 2 | 1 + 2 = 3 | **A** |
| 2 + 0 = 2 | 3 + 3 = 6 | 6 − 1 = 5 | 4 + 0 = 4 | 7 + 0 = 7 | |
| 5 + 1 = 6 | 2 + 5 = 7 | 2 + 4 = 6 | 3 + 2 = 5 | 4 + 0 = 4 | |
| 6 − 1 = 5 | 5 − 4 = 1 | 1 + 5 = 6 | 7 − 1 = 6 | 5 − 2 = 3 | **B** |
| 5 − 5 = 0 | 4 + 3 = 7 | 6 − 3 = 3 | 3 − 1 = 2 | 1 + 4 = 5 | |
| 6 − 0 = 6 | 4 + 3 = 7 | 5 − 2 = 3 | 3 + 3 = 6 | 4 − 0 = 4 | |
| 2 + 1 = 3 | 5 − 1 = 4 | 5 + 1 = 6 | 5 − 5 = 0 | 7 − 2 = 5 | **C** |
| 4 − 1 = 3 | 1 + 4 = 5 | 1 + 3 = 4 | 4 + 2 = 6 | 3 + 2 = 5 | |
| 1 + 0 = 1 | 3 − 3 = 0 | 3 + 4 = 7 | 4 − 4 = 0 | 2 + 3 = 5 | |
| 4 + 1 = 5 | 2 + 2 = 4 | 3 − 2 = 1 | 1 + 5 = 6 | 6 − 3 = 3 | **D** |
| 2 − 1 = 1 | 5 − 2 = 3 | 6 + 0 = 6 | 6 + 1 = 7 | 6 − 4 = 2 | |
| 5 + 1 = 6 | 6 − 4 = 2 | 7 − 2 = 5 | 7 − 0 = 7 | 3 + 3 = 6 | |
| 4 + 3 = 7 | 6 + 1 = 7 | 6 − 5 = 1 | 6 − 3 = 3 | 3 + 4 = 7 | **E** |
| 0 + 6 = 6 | 1 + 5 = 6 | 5 + 2 = 7 | 2 + 4 = 6 | 7 − 6 = 1 | |

Photocopy, then cut along the dotted lines so that each pair of players has a strip of 15 sums. Strip A is easier than the others; strip E contains only facts of 6 and 7. Use with gameboard on Shared Activity Book page 3.

**Y 1 T 2**
**Unit 2**

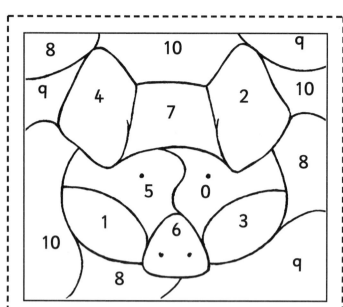

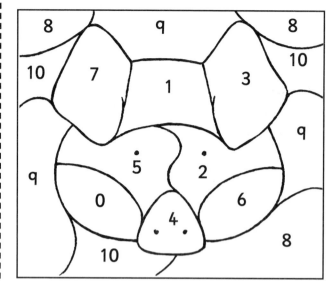

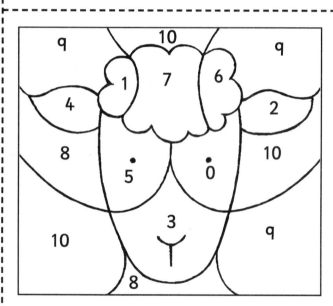

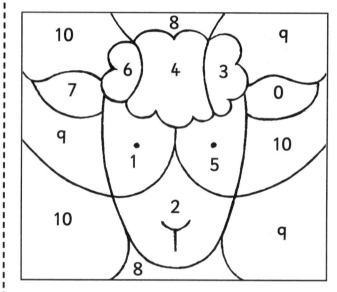

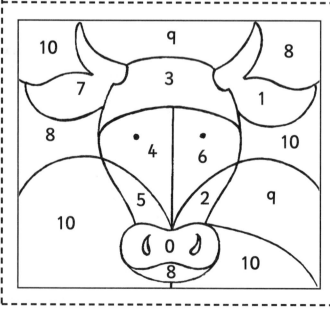

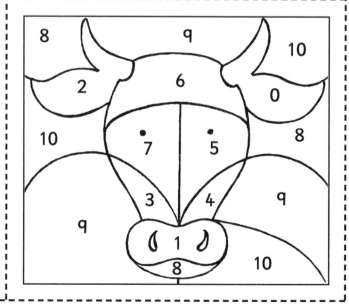

Photocopy, then cut up. Ask questions with answers 0, 1, 2, 3, 4, 5, 6 and 7. Children colour in a section which holds the answer. Copymaster can be used repeatedly for extra practice.

Y 1 T 2
Unit 3

# Number cards

| | | | |
|---|---|---|---|
| 10 | 7 | 9 | 8 |
| 3 | 6 | 4 | 2 |
| 10 | 7 | 9 | 8 |
| 3 | 6 | 4 | 2 |

Photocopy Copymaster 4 back to back with Copymaster 5, then laminate if possible and cut into 2 sets of 8 cards for each pair of players. Use with gameboard on Shared Activity Book page 5.

**Y 1 T 2**
**Unit 3**

# Picture jigsaw

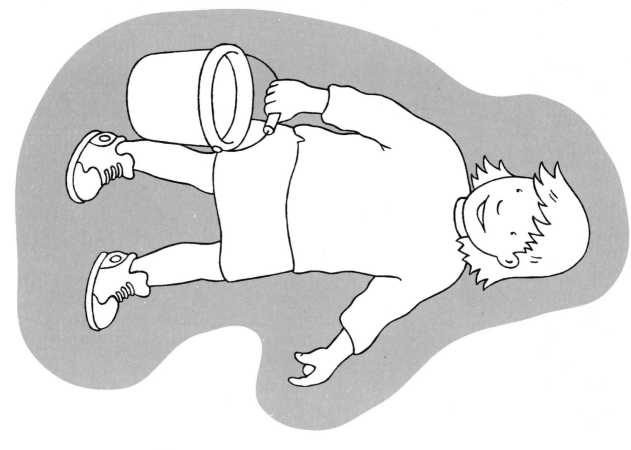

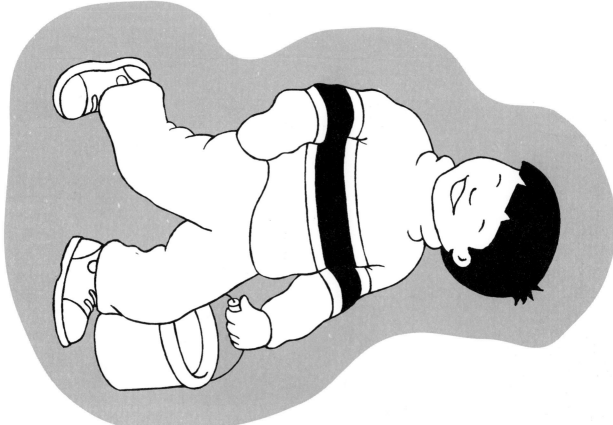

Photocopy Copymaster 4 back to back with Copymaster 5, then laminate if possible and cut into 2 sets of 8 cards for each pair of players. Use with gameboard on Shared Activity Book page 5.

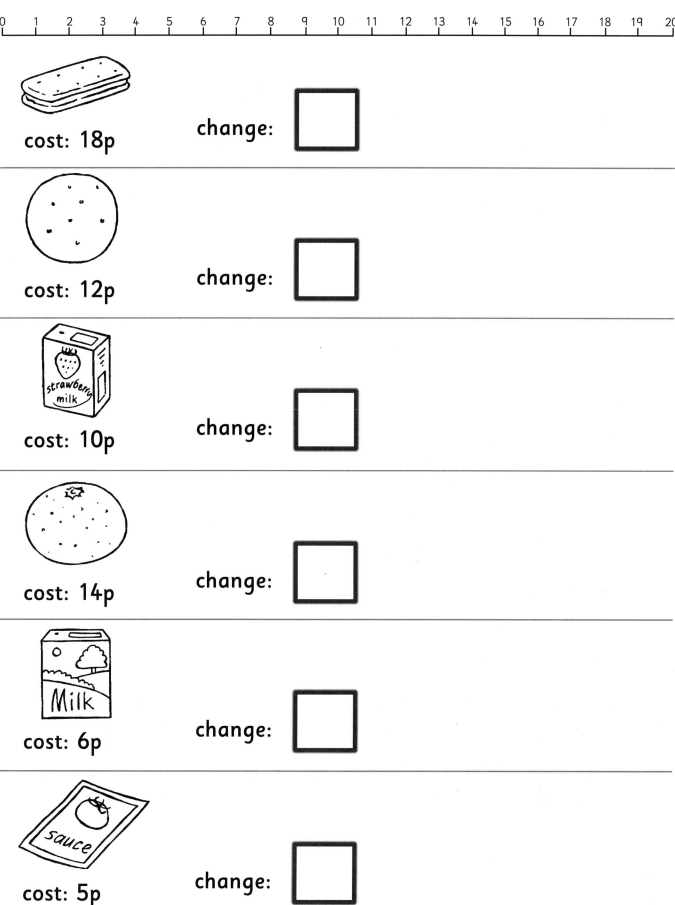

0 1 2 3 4 5 6 7 8 9 10 11 12 13 14 15 16 17 18 19 20

cost: 18p    change:

cost: 12p    change:

cost: 10p    change:

cost: 14p    change:

cost: 6p    change:

cost: 5p    change:

Photocopy and issue one per child. Children use coins and the number line, draw circles to represent coins and write in their value.

Y 1 T 2
Unit 4

# Z Estimate mass

How many _____ does each weigh?

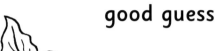

| good guess | weigh |
|---|---|

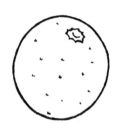

Before you make multiple copies of this sheet, draw and/or write in the unit of measure to be used – in the heading and beside each box – on one copy. The sheet can be reissued using a different unit of measure.

Y 1 T 2
Unit 5

How many marbles?

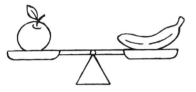  

How many monkeys?

How many penguins?

How many cubes?

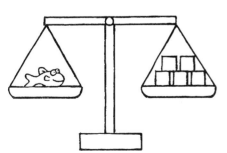 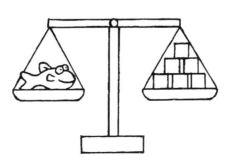 

Mask off part of the sheet before photocopying or cut the sheet into sections if required. Issue one sheet per pair.

Y 1 T 2
Unit 5

43

**Pet show data pictures**

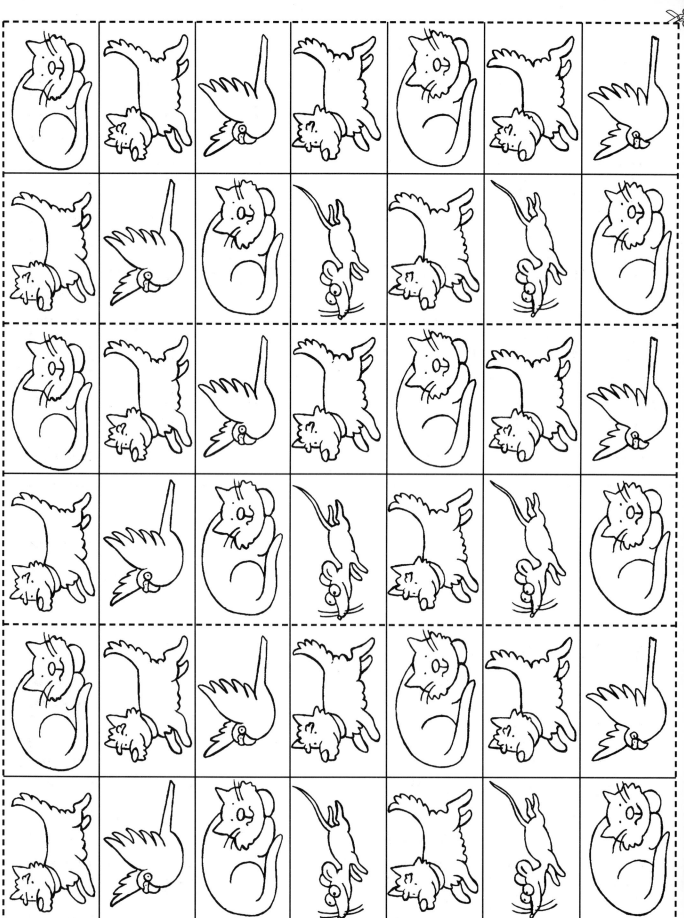

Use with Recording Book page 29. Photocopy one sheet for every three children. Cut into strips before issuing.

Y 1 T 2
Unit 12

# Add/subtract within 12

## Addition within 12

3 + 6 = ☐          10 + 2 = ☐

5 + 3 = ☐          7 + 3 = ☐

8 + 4 = ☐          5 + 6 = ☐

5 + 7 = ☐          1 + 11 = ☐

9 + 3 = ☐          12 + 0 = ☐

## Subtraction within 12

3 − 0 = ☐          12 − 12 = ☐

10 − 3 = ☐          12 − 6 = ☐

12 − 2 = ☐          8 − 5 = ☐

11 − 4 = ☐          12 − 0 = ☐

12 − 8 = ☐          6 − 4 = ☐

Mask off part of the sheet or photocopy only one half to provide the required task.

Y 1 T 2
Unit 12

# Z **Parent's guide**
## to the Homework Sheets

IMPORTANT INFORMATION   There are 10 Homework Sheets for each term.
(First, last and assessment weeks have no homework.) The Homework Sheet will
usually be given to your child on **Thursday** and should be brought back to school on .............................

Please remember to send it
back on that day!

This 'Need' box shows the
**materials** needed for the
activity.

The activity follows up something being learned in
class in the current week.
It is meant to provide extra practice for the child
and to give you an opportunity to see what your
child is doing in school.
It should be fun (we want your child to enjoy
maths!), so please give encouragement and a little
help if needed. 10–15 minutes is the average time
which should be spent on the activity, and never
more than 30 minutes.

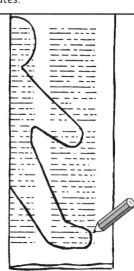
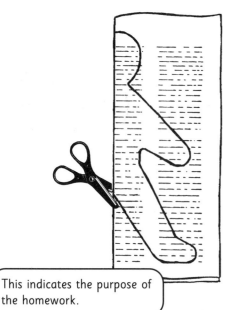
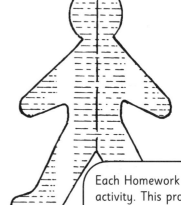

Each Homework Sheet has an extra
activity. This provides another idea
for an activity you can do with your
child – if you have time and if your
child is not overtired!

This indicates the purpose of
the homework.

This gives you instructions
for doing the activity.

**Key idea**   Folding a shape in half and making into a
symmetrical pattern.
Your child folds a sheet of newspaper in half, draws half a man against
the fold, cuts round the line and opens out the shape.
Have you made a man? Is he folded in half? Are both sides the same?

**Optional extra**   Make a list of some items
in the house which are circle shaped,
e.g. plate, clock face.

# Mystery addition

Name

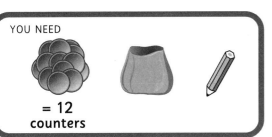

= 12 counters

EXAMPLE

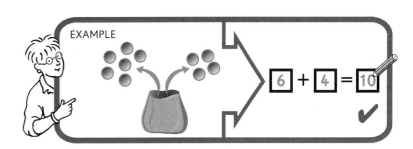

$6 + 4 = 10$ ✔

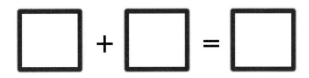

☐ + ☐ = ☐      ☐ + ☐ = ☐

☐ + ☐ = ☐      ☐ + ☐ = ☐

☐ + ☐ = ☐      ☐ + ☐ = ☐

☐ + ☐ = ☐      ☐ + ☐ = ☐

☐ + ☐ = ☐      ☐ + ☐ = ☐

**Key idea** Understanding addition.

Place 12 counters (or buttons, marbles, etc.) in a bag. Without looking, your child takes out 2 handfuls. Then they count each handful and write the numbers in the boxes, add the numbers together and write the answer. Explain that the counters are to be put back into the bag after each sum.

**Optional extra** Play a quiz game of all the pairs of numbers which add to 10.

Y 1 T 2
Unit 2

# ☰ Toy shop sale

Name

YOU NEED

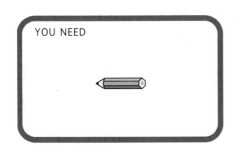

EXAMPLE

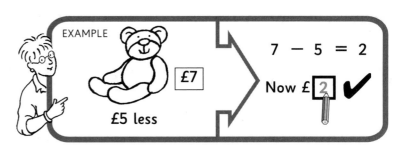

£7

£5 less

7 − 5 = 2

Now £ 2 ✔

£9

£2 less.    Now £ ☐

£12

£5 less.    Now £ ☐

£5

£1 less.    Now £ ☐

£70

£10 less.    Now £ ☐

£30

£10 less.    Now £ ☐

£12

£3 less.    Now £ ☐

**Key idea**   Understanding subtraction.
Your child looks at the price, subtracts the amount less and
writes the answer in the box.

**Optional extra**   Make a list of the subtraction
facts for 7.
Start with 7 − 0 = 7,
    then 7 − 1 = 6, etc.

Y 1 T 2
Unit 3

# z Pocket money

Name

YOU NEED

EXAMPLE

= 19p

19p ✓

Match

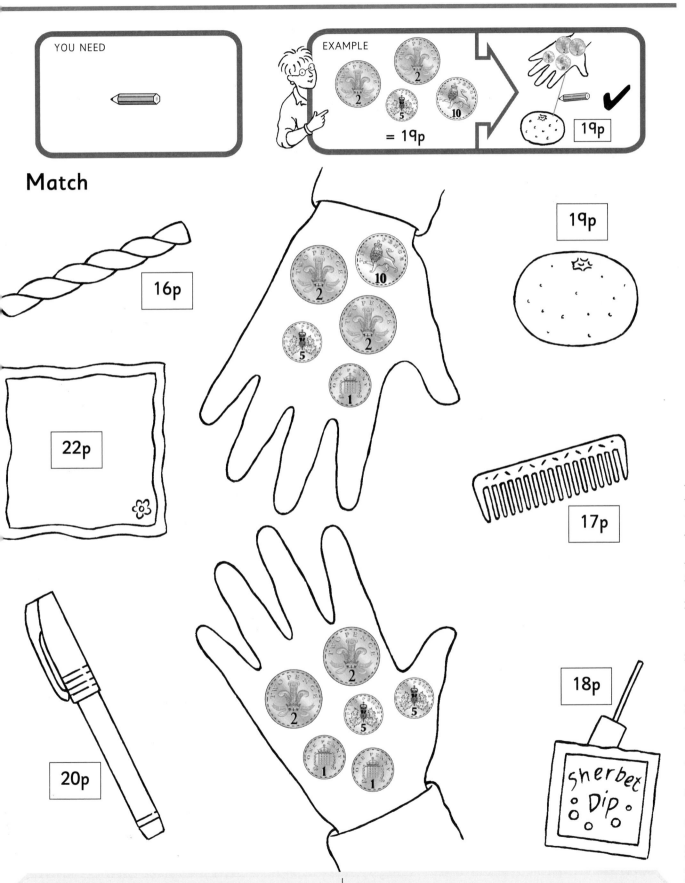

16p

19p

22p

17p

20p

18p

sherbet Dip

**Key idea** Solving simple money problems.

Explain that your child is going to 'spend' the pocket money. Count the money in the hand and draw a line to match it to the item which costs exactly that amount.

**Optional extra** Lay out coins to make amounts within 20p, e.g. make 13p, 16p, 17p.

Y 1 T 2
Unit 4

# How heavy?

Name

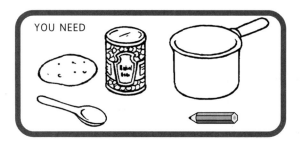

YOU NEED

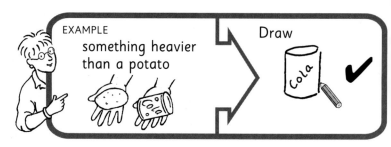

EXAMPLE
something heavier
than a potato

Draw

Cola ✔

## Draw something **heavier** than

 a potato

 a spoon

## Draw something **lighter** than

a tin of beans

a saucepan

**Key idea**   Comparing two masses.

Your child holds the potato in one hand and holds something in the other hand to compare and decide whether it is heavier than the potato. When a heavier object is found your child draws it in the box. Then compare other items.

**Optional extra**   Give your child 3 different objects and ask for them to be put in order from lightest to heaviest.

 Y 1 T 2
Unit 5

# Make a man

Name

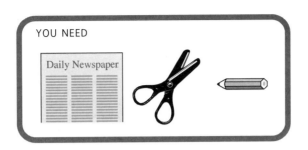

YOU NEED

Daily Newspaper

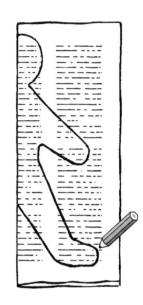

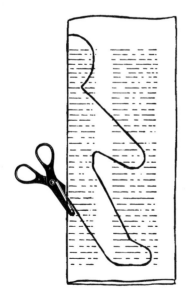

**Key idea**  Folding a shape in half and making it into a symmetrical pattern.

Your child folds a sheet of newspaper in half, draws half a man against the fold, cuts round the line and opens out the shape.
Have you made a man? Is he folded in half? Are both sides the same?

**Optional extra**  Make a list of some items in the house which are circle shaped, e.g. plate.

Y 1 T 2
Unit 6

# Z Odd or even

Name

YOU NEED

real objects to count

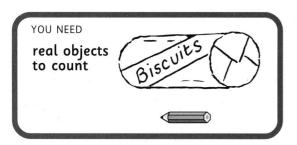

EXAMPLE

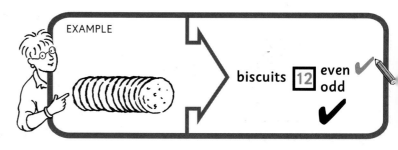

biscuits [12] even ✓
odd
✔

? slices ☐ even
odd

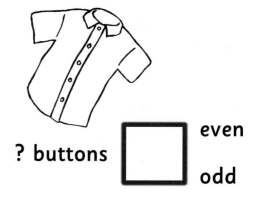

? buttons ☐ even
odd

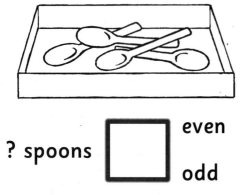

? spoons ☐ even
odd

My Story Book

? pages ☐ even
odd

- - - - - - - - ☐ even
odd

**Key idea**  Counting a number of objects and saying whether it is an odd or an even number.
Let your child look at the *real* objects, count and write the number in the box. They then decide whether the number is an odd or an even number (perhaps by pairing the objects), and ticks the correct label. Find something else to count (a number between 5 and 30), then your child draws it at the bottom of the page and answers the questions.

**Optional extra**
Practise counting in twos or in fives from 0 to 20 and back again.

Y 1 T 2
Unit 8

# Z About turn

Name

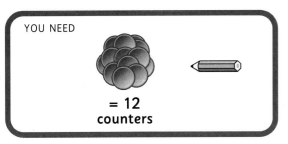

YOU NEED

= 12
counters

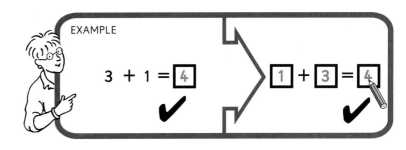

EXAMPLE

$3 + 1 = \boxed{4}$  ✔    $\boxed{1} + \boxed{3} = \boxed{4}$  ✔

$5 + 2 = \boxed{\phantom{0}}$     $\boxed{\phantom{0}} + \boxed{\phantom{0}} = \boxed{\phantom{0}}$

$3 + 6 = \boxed{\phantom{0}}$     $\boxed{\phantom{0}} + \boxed{\phantom{0}} = \boxed{\phantom{0}}$

$4 + 2 = \boxed{\phantom{0}}$     $\boxed{\phantom{0}} + \boxed{\phantom{0}} = \boxed{\phantom{0}}$

$5 + 6 = \boxed{\phantom{0}}$     $\boxed{\phantom{0}} + \boxed{\phantom{0}} = \boxed{\phantom{0}}$

$7 + 3 = \boxed{\phantom{0}}$     $\boxed{\phantom{0}} + \boxed{\phantom{0}} = \boxed{\phantom{0}}$

**Key idea**  Understanding that addition can be done in any order. Your child adds the numbers together and writes the total in the box. Then they write the numbers in the reverse order and add them again. Are the answers the same for each pair? Counters, marbles, buttons, etc. may be used to help with the addition.

**Optional extra**  Two players hold out a number of fingers. Take turns to find the difference between the numbers by subtracting the smaller number from the larger. Score a point if correct.

Y 1 T 2
Unit 9

53

# Make the money

Name

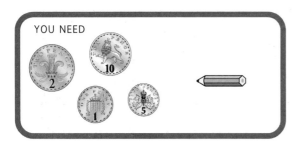

YOU NEED

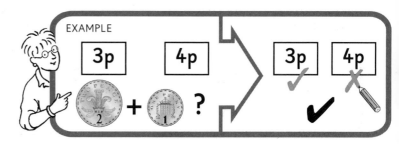

EXAMPLE

3p    4p    ➤    3p ✓    4p ✗

2 + 1 = ?    ✔

| 1p | 2p | 3p | 4p | 5p |
|---|---|---|---|---|

| 6p | 7p | 8p | 9p | 10p |
|---|---|---|---|---|

| 11p | 12p | 13p | 14p | 15p |
|---|---|---|---|---|

| 16p | 17p | 18p | | |
|---|---|---|---|---|

**Key idea**   Using coins to make exact amounts.
Your child uses the coins to find out if the amount can be made using the coins 1p, 2p, 5p and 10p. Tick the box for yes, if it can be made, and put a cross if the exact amount cannot be made.

**Optional extra**   Shop play: work out the change from 12p when paying for amounts between 1p and 12p.

 Y 1 T 2
Unit 10

**Evening events**

Name

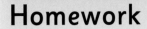

YOU NEED

EXAMPLE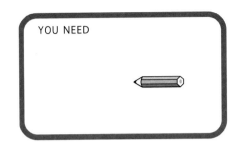

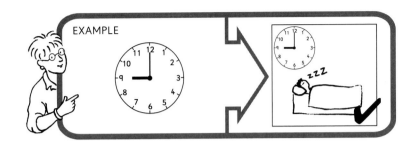

**Key idea** Understanding time.
Your child reads the time on each clock, then draws a simple picture to show what they were doing at that time.

**Optional extra** How many hops can you do in one minute? Make a 'good guess' first, then count how many you can do. Was it a 'good guess'?

**Y 1 T 2**
**Unit 11**

# Find the favourite

COPYMASTER 21
**Homework**

Name

YOU NEED

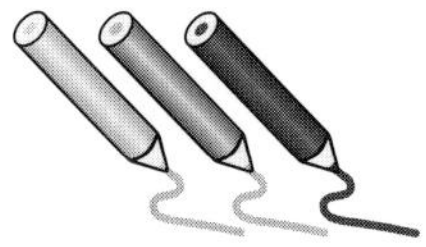

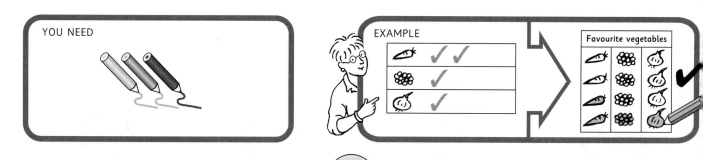

EXAMPLE

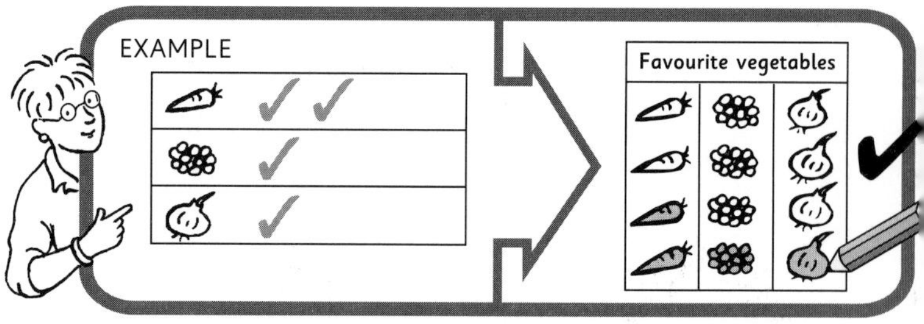


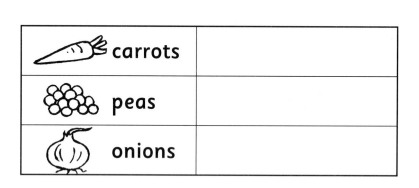

| | |
|---|---|
| 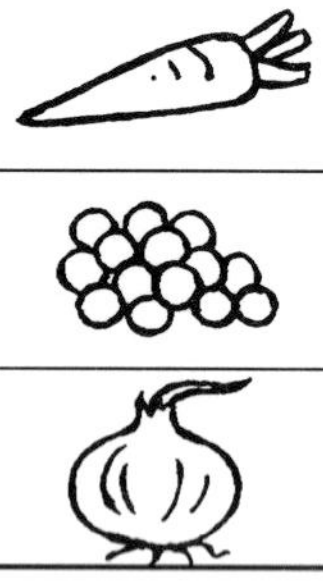 carrots | |
| peas | |
| onions | |

## Favourite vegetables

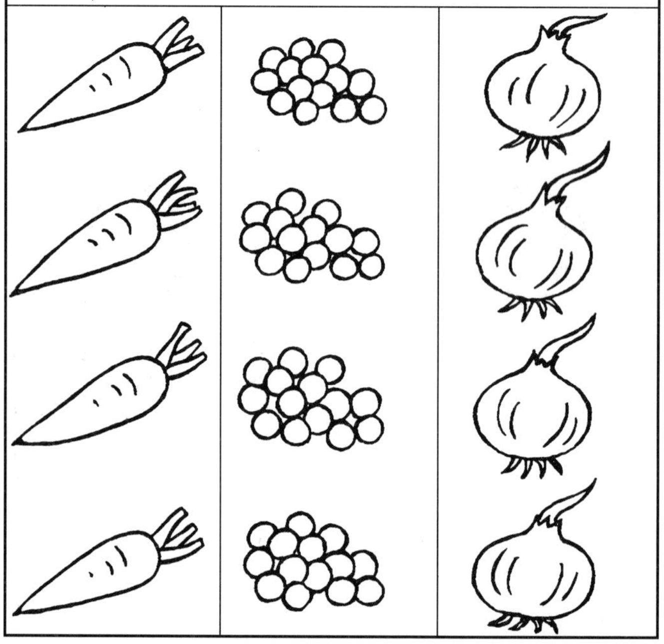

**Key idea** Solving a problem by organising information.
Your child asks 4 people which vegetable they prefer: carrots, peas or onions, and ticks to record their answers. Then they count the ticks and colour the right number of pictures on the chart to show this information.

**Optional extra** Play a quiz game for addition and subtraction facts within 8. i.e. 8 – 0 = 8, 8 – 1 = 7 etc.

Y 1 T 2
Unit 12

# Numbers 0–10

| 0 | 1 | 2 | 3 |
|---|---|---|---|
| 4 | 5 | 6 | 7 |
| 8 | 9 | 10 | + |

Photocopy, laminate (or paste onto card) and cut into separate cards. Make a set for each child. These will be used frequently in mental and main session activities. (This creates cards of the same size as NES-Arnold NB 9734/3 which come pre-prepared.)

**Y 1 T 2**

# Numbers 11–20

| 11 | 12 | 13 | 14 |
| --- | --- | --- | --- |
| 15 | 16 | 17 | 18 |
| 19 | 20 | – | = |

Photocopy, laminate (or paste onto card) and cut into separate cards. Make a set for each child. These will be used frequently in mental and main session activities. (This creates cards of the same size as NES-Arnold NB 9734/3, which come pre-prepared.)

Y 1 T 2

# Arrow cards 0–29

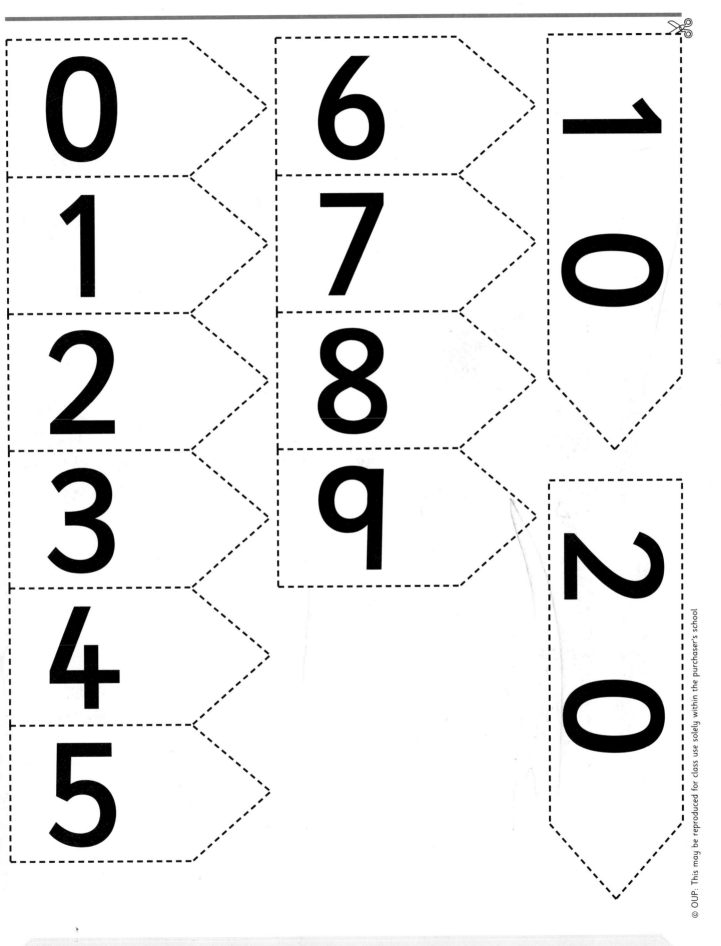

Photocopy, laminate (or paste onto card) and cut into separate cards. Make one set for demonstrating place value by placing the units card over the tens card, aligning the arrows.

Y 1 T 2

# Year 1 Record-keeping Grid

This sheet may be used to collate information from individual records for each term, or to collate records over the full year.

| Numbers and the number system | | | | | | | | | | | | | | | | | | | | | | |
|---|---|---|---|---|---|---|---|---|---|---|---|---|---|---|---|---|---|---|---|---|---|---|
| counting; properties of nos; no. sequences | | | | | | | | | | | | | | | | | | | | | | |
| place value and ordering | | | | | | | | | | | | | | | | | | | | | | |
| estimating | | | | | | | | | | | | | | | | | | | | | | |
| **Calculations** | | | | | | | | | | | | | | | | | | | | | | |
| understanding addition | | | | | | | | | | | | | | | | | | | | | | |
| understanding subtraction | | | | | | | | | | | | | | | | | | | | | | |
| rapid recall of + & – facts | | | | | | | | | | | | | | | | | | | | | | |
| mental calculation strategies (+ & –) | | | | | | | | | | | | | | | | | | | | | | |
| **Solving problems** | | | | | | | | | | | | | | | | | | | | | | |
| making decisions | | | | | | | | | | | | | | | | | | | | | | |
| reasoning about numbers or shapes | | | | | | | | | | | | | | | | | | | | | | |
| 'real life' money or measure problems | | | | | | | | | | | | | | | | | | | | | | |
| organising and using data | | | | | | | | | | | | | | | | | | | | | | |
| **Measures, shape and space** | | | | | | | | | | | | | | | | | | | | | | |
| measures | | | | | | | | | | | | | | | | | | | | | | |
| measures: time | | | | | | | | | | | | | | | | | | | | | | |
| shape and space | | | | | | | | | | | | | | | | | | | | | | |